There goes that song again

ONE HUNDRED YEARS OF POPULAR SONG

COMPILED AND WRITTEN
BY COLIN WALSH

Elm Tree Books
EMI Music Publishing

First published in Great Britain 1977 by
Elm Tree Books Ltd
90 Great Russell Street, London WC1B 3PT
in association with
EMI Music Publishing Ltd
138–140 Charing Cross Road, London WC2H 0LD
Introduction and text © 1977, EMI Music Publishing Ltd
For copyright of songs see individual copyright notices

ISBN 241 89664 9

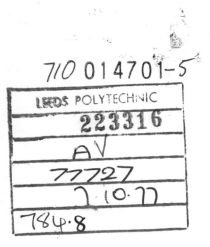
Designed by Book Production Consultants,
7 Brooklands Avenue, Cambridge.

Jacket designed by Lawrence Edwards

Music Editor Cecil Bolton

Printed in Great Britain by West Central Printing Co., Ltd

CONTENTS

ACKNOWLEDGEMENTS

Music is so much part of our lives, and its influences so much part of our everyday existence, that we must all carry in our minds a store of songs, tunes and melodies on which we can draw when the occasion demands. My particular store comes from a number of different sources and I have to acknowledge the influence of my parents. They both played in bands before the war, they ran a record shop which gave me hundreds of old 78s to play about with, and they put me on the stage from the age of three, which, whatever it did for the suffering audience, at least gave me a vast repertoire of songs to gurgle in the bath.

To be precise, therefore, in acknowledging all the sources which have shaped this book is a difficult task. However, there are those who have contributed directly to this publication and my thanks are due to Pat Howgill for both advice and freedom which allowed me to select the material I considered appropriate; to Kay O'Dwyer and Bert Corri for giving me the background to Tin Pan Alley in general and Francis, Day & Hunter in particular; to Harry Shaberman for help in sifting through the vast catalogue of F, D & H and for leading me out of a number of blind alleys; and to Chris Ellis who must surely have the most encyclopaedic knowledge of popular music to be found in the business.

Thanks also to Mrs Cecile d'Amato and Nigel Sisson for allowing me to plunder their extensive collection of journals, magazines and periodicals on popular music, and likewise to Peter Hepple, Editor of *The Stage*, for a similar plundering of *The Stage* archives.

BBC Radio's *Ragtime to Rock 'n' Roll*, produced by John Billingham, gave me an excellent yardstick against which to measure the development of popular music and much insight into the influences of change.

Finally, of the literally thousands of books and magazines which have been published in the last fifty years, I must acknowledge below the following publications as providing source material for this book. A special mention should be made of the prodigious work of Leslie Lowe in compiling the *Directory of Popular Music* (Peterson Publishing Co. Ltd) which must surely be the most valuable reference book on popular music today.

After the Ball by Ian Whitcomb, Allen Lane 1973
A History of Popular Music in America by Sigmund Spaeth, Phoenix House 1948
All You Need is Love by Tony Palmer, Weidenfeld & Nicholson and Chappell 1976
America Sings by Carl L. Carmer, Farrar & Rinehart 1942
British Music Hall by Mander & Mitchenson, Studio Vista 1965
Down Beat, 608 South Dearborn, Chicago, USA
Melody Maker, IPC Business Press Ltd (to whom thanks should also be made for allowing me to consult the archives)
Mastertone, published by Gibson Inc., Kalamazoo, Michigan, USA
Music Hall Songbook by Peter Gammond, David & Charles 1975
Sixty Years of Music Hall by J. Garrett, Chappell/Deutsch 1976
The A to Z of Rock and Roll, Studio Vista 1971
The Big Bands by George Simon, Macmillan Co., New York 1967
The Dance Band Era by Albert McCarthy, Studio Vista 1971
The Jazz Scene by Francis Newton, MacGibbon & Kee 1961
The Rise and Fall of Tin Pan Alley, Funk and Wagnalls 1964
The Sound of the City by Charles Gillett, Souvenir Press 1970
The Story of Francis, Day and Hunter by John Abbott, Francis, Day & Hunter 1952
They're Playing Our Song by Max Wilk, W. H. Allen 1973
Tin Pan Alley by Eddie Rogers, Robert Hale Ltd 1964
Tin Pan Alley by Ian Whitcomb, Wildwood House/EMI Music Publishing 1975
Your Own, Your Very Own by Peter Gammond, Ian Allen 1971

WARM UP

What makes a song popular? It is not an easy question to answer. A witty lyric, an appealing tune, a fashionable singer, an exciting rhythm, a tugging at the heart strings – all these attributes can make a listener want to hear that song again. But *lasting* popularity needs something more; it needs originality and nostalgia.

Nostalgia is much in vogue today. Even the most recent decade, the Sixties, is acquiring that patina of nostalgia which makes a Beatles' song something of a period piece. A song is a snatch of memory which you can take with you through life; it can evoke a time in life which you want to remember. So long as nostalgia does not smother the desire for something new, it is no bad thing. It enables us to catch again the rhythm of ragtime, the relaxation of the crooner, even the idiocy of a chorus of *I'm Henery the Eighth, I Am!*

But a popular song is more than something original or nostalgic. It has to be worth remembering, not easily forgotten. Not always to your taste, perhaps, but significant enough to survive.

The songs in this book have survived, survived even among the abundance of choice offered today. It is a little hard, in 1977, to envisage which of our current hits will be around during the next fifty years, which tunes today's teeny-boppers will be humming nostalgically in the 1990s. The chances of survival seem to become more slim as the pace grows faster; the competition is great. But a few will stand out sufficiently to cover us for the next hundred years; no single generation has the right to decide on the terms of popularity.

The songs included here are, of course, an arbitrary selection from literally thousands of songs which we could call 'popular'. They follow a chronological sequence and they all appear here because a lot of people have enjoyed hearing them, singing them and playing them.

They have something else in common – they all carry the Francis, Day & Hunter imprint. What better way to explore a hundred years of popular song than to follow the fortunes of a major song publisher, itself now a century old and still scoring hits.

In 1877 the firm of F, D & H was born out of the clamour and excitement of the Music Halls of Britain and the folksy plaintiveness of the minstrels of the United States. Not a bad combination of parents for a musical babe destined to become a central figure in popularising songs.

Fifty years later the gramophone, the radio and the talking pictures were making songs popular in a matter of weeks on both sides of the Atlantic. A foot on both shores was a wise investment for the future.

F, D & H was founded as a business to publish popular songs, an aim which was to be steadily achieved over the next hundred years. The emphasis is on the word 'popular', a song 'adapted to the understanding, taste, or means of the people' as the dictionary rather pompously tells us. There was little point in trying to create a successful business out of unpopular songs, however meritworthy they may have been in themselves. The songs had to 'catch on'.

And catch on they did. I am not attempting, in the following chapters, to write a history of popular music: I am setting the stage for standards. Inevitably, there are many omissions, but the task of compiling a list of the thousands who have contributed, in one form or another, to the music that has influenced our lives in the past hundred years is one that could fill many volumes and take many years to complete. This book is to remind you of the songs that you have not forgotten. Few people will turn these pages without finding at least one song which stirs their memory, one chorus which sets a foot tapping.

So here's your chance to enjoy those songs again. Push out the Old Joanna and turn to page 11. The show's all yours.

SUNG BY Mr JAMES FRANCIS OF THE

MOHAWK MINSTRELS

AGRICULTURAL HALL, LONDON.

ON MONDAY I MET MARY ANN.

On Monday I met Mary Ann, on Tuesday Mary Jane,
On Wednesday I met Miss McCann, on Thursday Kitty Payne
On Friday Betty Hopkinson, on Saturday Miss Small,
On Sunday night I stayed at home for fear I'd meet them all.

WRITTEN BY
HARRY HUNTER.

COMPOSED BY
DAVID DAY.

LONDON FRANCIS BROTHERS & DAY, BLENHEIM HOUSE, OXFORD ST W.

6

1
PLAYING THE HALLS

Lottie Collins

James Francis

Harry Hunter

Music Hall. Gas-lamp flares, jostling cabs in wet streets, posters in huge black type, sweating faces, clinking glasses, waxed moustaches.

Music Hall. Crashing applause, yawning curtains, tuning-up instruments, bellowing choruses in the gallery, gold-lacquered cupids, feather-boa'd tarts.

Music Hall. The Roll of Honour: George Leybourne, Arthur Roberts, G. H. Chirgyn, Dan Leno, Eugene Stratton, Albert Chevalier, Tom Costello, Gus Ellen, Vesta Tilley, Mark Sheridan, Little Tich, Harold Champion, George Robey, Nellie Wallace, Marie Lloyd, Harry Lauder, Harry Tate, Vesta Victoria, Florrie Forde, Wilkie Bard, Billie Merson, G. H. Elliot, Will Fyffe and dozens of others who gave their all in the Great Halls of Fame.

Two words that meant something to everybody; the first of the mass entertainments. The railways could not only shunt coal to southern fireplaces; they could shunt the dandified Lion Comiques like George Leybourne from the Tivoli in London to the Parthenon Music Hall in Liverpool. London led, of course, with over two hundred music halls in the 1870s, but the provinces boasted some three hundred even though only a few, such as the Argyle in Birkenhead, could match the opulence of the Oxford or the Pavilion.

With twenty or more artists on the same bill, there was a great demand for the new breed of professionals who could face the lights in any town and belt out, over the noise and clatter of the audience, the current popular song. And, as that song, when it really caught on, could sell over a quarter of a million copies (as compared with sales of about five thousand copies for a Top Twenty hit of a century later), it was a logical step for two enterprising brothers, William and James Francis, to embark on a future in music publishing.

The musical roots of the two brothers were not, however, in the barely respectable music halls but in the more sedate family entertainment offered by the minstrelsy. A completely American institution dating back to the 1830s, the minstrelsy had become an established entertainment in England in the 1840s after its introduction in London by Thomas Rice in 1837. The minstrels, blacking their faces and cultivating an impression of child-like naivety on the part of the negro, gave out, with a combination of comic songs backed by the banjo – like *Zip-Coon Turkey In The Straw* – and 'white spirituals', a mixture of hymns and negro religious music such as *Star In The East*.

When the Francis Brothers formed the Mohawk Minstrels in 1873, their troupe found immediate popularity and sold out to audiences which numbered some three thousand a night by 1877. They had, by this date, been joined by a writer of songs, gags and sketches who had been poached from a rival group of Manhattan Minstrels. Harry Hunter's fertile song-writing talent had become the life-blood of the Mohawks, and William and James decided that a publishing outlet was needed for the Mohawks' popular songs.

The Mohawks Minstrel Magazine, or Harry Hunter's Vocal Annual, was published by the Francis Brothers and David Day, a newly-acquired partner with much experience culled from the music publishers Ascherberg, Hopwood & Crewe. The album was much plagiarised by other troupes, there being, as yet, no copyright protection to jog the tender conscience.

But minstrelsy was on the way out. The humour and pathos of Music Hall, concentrating on the hardship of life and its working-class pageant of wash-day, large families, funerals and marital relations, found a more familiar chord of response in the lower classes than the more restricted sentiments of the minstrels. Collins and the Canterbury Arms held more attractions in the 1880s than the Mohawks in the Agricultural Hall, and David Day, with an ear for a good song and the energy to go from hall to hall each night, proved to be the pillar which supported the advance of the Francis, Day & Hunter imprint into popular song publishing. Although the name Hunter is retained to the present day, Harry was never more than a sleeping partner, being more at home in front of the lights than behind them. He had joined the company on the death of James Francis but enthusiasm waned and he sold out his interests in 1900.

Vesta Tilley

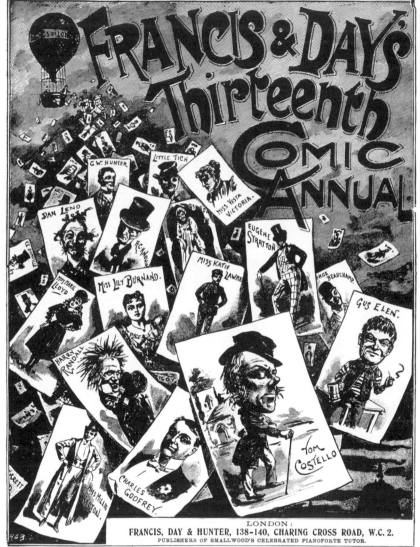

George Robey

Music Hall, and its close relation variety, were to remain the dominant forms of entertainment until the 1920s when competition from the cheap silent cinema was to mark the demise of the former, leaving variety to struggle on until the 'talkies' took over most of the theatres.

Essentially Music Hall was concerned with singers and the songs that became part of their repertoire. Harry Champion could no more be divorced from *I'm Henery The Eighth, I Am!* and *Boiled Beef And Carrots* than Harry Lauder from *I Love A Lassie* and *Roamin' In The Gloamin'*. The audience wanted to identify with the sentiments of the songs and the style of the singers and the genteel drawing-room ballads had to give way to the more comic, sometimes more vulgar and generally more boisterous songs of the *people's entertainers*.

8

The singers needed good lungs to penetrate to the back of the packed halls. Marie Lloyd could hardly whisper *Its A Bit Of A Ruin That Cromwell Knocked About A Bit* and her death in 1922 marked the end of the whole breed of 'belters'. Microphones were despised and distrusted well into the 1930s and even today there are those for whom a singer is only worth the name if Middle C shatters the gallery.

Music Hall songs, therefore, were written for an audience that liked to join in with the chorus, a characteristic that keeps many of the tunes alive today. There were, of course, those that told a richly-sentimental story as in Leo Dryden's *The Miner's Dream Of Home* and those that brought a tear to the eye, as Albert Chevalier's *My Old Dutch*, but it was a rousing chorus of *Ta-Ra-Ra-Boom-De-Ay* which got the gallery going.

Marie Lloyd

THE STAGE YEAR BOOK.

LONDON MUSIC HALLS.

Hall.	Booking Circuit (or Manager's Name).	Rehearsal.	Telephone.
ALEXANDRA PALACE	E. Goodship	—	Finchley 41
ALHAMBRA	Geo. Scott	12 noon	Gerrard 5060-5065
BALHAM EMPIRE	—	—	—
BATTERSEA (CRYSTAL) EMPIRE	Brammal	—	Battersea 1476
BEDFORD	Day's	1 p.m.	North 709
BOW PALACE	Macnaghten's	12 noon	East 417
CAMBERWELL EMPIRE	Sparrow & Rawn	2 p.m.	Brixton 905
CAMBERWELL PALACE	Stoll's	2 p.m.	Hop 1098
CANTERBURY	Syndicate Halls	11 a.m.	Hop 726
CHELSEA PALACE	Syndicate Halls	12 noon	Kensington 733
CLAPHAM GRAND	Gibbons'	2 p.m.	Battersea 88
CROUCH END HIPPODROME	L.C.C.	—	Hornsey 420
CROYDON EMPIRE PALACE	Gibbons'	1 p.m.	Croydon 174
CRYSTAL PALACE	—	—	Sydenham 23-168
DUCHESS, BALHAM	Gibbons'	1.30 p.m.	Battersea 1058
EALING HIPPODROME	Gibbons'	12.30 p.m	Ealing 1056
EAST HAM PALACE	Syndicate Halls	4 p.m.	Barking 54
EMPIRE, LEICESTER SQUARE	H. J. Hitchins	12 noon	Gerrard 2577, 5140 / Central 7768
EMPRESS, BRIXTON	Syndicate Halls	1 p.m.	Brixton 41
EUSTON	Syndicate Halls	12 noon	North 627
FORESTERS	Macnaghten's	12 noon	Avenue 5954
GRANVILLE	Stoll's	3 p.m.	Kennington 206
GREENWICH PALACE	Barnard's	2 p.m.	Deptford 125
HACKNEY EMPIRE	Stoll's	1 p.m.	Dalston 3
HAMMERSMITH PALACE	L.C.C.	1.30 p.m.	Hammersmith 106
HENGLER'S CIRCUS	M. Beketow	—	Gerrard 4138
HOLBORN EMPIRE	Gibbons	—	Holborn 5567
HOLLOWAY EMPIRE	Stoll's	1 p.m.	North 600
ILFORD	Syndicate Halls	Not yet built	
ISLINGTON EMPIRE	Gibbons'	1 p.m.	North 802
ISLINGTON GRAND	Gibbons'	12 noon	North 571
ISLINGTON HIPPODROME (COLLINS)	L.C.C.	1.30 p.m.	North 658
KINGSTON-ON-THAMES		Now in course of erection	
LONDON COLISEUM	Stoll's	10 a.m.	Gerrard 7451-7544
LONDON HIPPODROME	Stoll's	12 noon	Gerrard 1399-2321 / 4015-5526
LONDON PAVILION	F. Glenister	12 noon	Gerrard 2619-3886
METROPOLITAN	Syndicate Halls	1 p.m.	Paddington 194
MIDDLESEX	Graydon	2 p.m.	Gerrard 2984
NEW CROSS EMPIRE	Stoll's	1 p.m.	Deptford 245
OXFORD	Syndicate Halls	12.30	Gerrard 2934
PALACE, W.	Alfred Butt	11.30	Gerrard 6844 4144
PARAGON	Syndicate Halls	11 a.m.	East 165
POPLAR HIPPODROME	Gibbons'	1 p.m.	East 64
PUTNEY HIPPODROME	Gibbons'	12 noon	Putney 808
QUEEN'S, POPLAR	Jack Woolf	1 p.m.	East 714
RICHMOND	Stoll's	2 p.m.	Richmond 91
ROTHERHITHE HIPPODROME	Gibbons'	1 p.m.	Hop 1134
ROYAL ALBERT, CANNING TOWN	Closed	—	East 1076
ROYAL STANDARD	T. S. Dickie	1 p.m.	Westminster 503
ROYAL VICTOR, CANNING TOWN	Closed	—	—
SADLER'S WELLS	Macnaghten	12 noon	Central 5890
SHEPHERD'S BUSH EMPIRE	Stoll's	1 p.m.	Hammersmith 106
SHOREDITCH EMPIRE (LONDON)	L.C.C.	1.30 p.m.	Wall 3647
SHOREDITCH HIPPODROME (CAMBRIDGE)	L.C.C.	1 p.m.	Wall 3505
SHOREDITCH OLYMPIA (STANDARD)	Gibbons	—	Wall 1693
SOUTH LONDON PALACE	Syndicate Halls	12 noon	Hop 912
STAR, BERMONDSEY	J. Bass	—	Hop 1048
STOKE NEWINGTON PALACE	De Freece	1 p.m.	Dalston 85
STRATFORD EMPIRE	Stoll's	1 p.m.	East 861
SURREY	Macnaghten	12 noon	Hop 1460
TIVOLI	Syndicate Halls	11.30 a.m.	Gerrard 2584
WALTHAMSTOW PALACE	Syndicate Halls	3 p.m.	Walthamstow 40
WILLESDEN HIPPODROME	Gibbons'	12.30 p.m.	North 804
WOOLWICH HIPPODROME	Gibbons'	1 p.m.	Woolwich 69-85

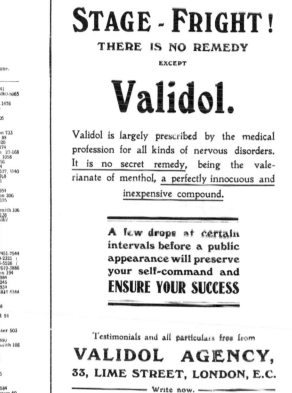
By 1897, when expansion brought F, D & H from Oxford Street to 142 Charing Cross Road, the cult of the minstrels was nearly over and the company was becoming firmly established as a leading publisher of popular songs. David Day, comfortably established in the driving seat, was building up a staff which included Edgar Bateman (*If It Wasn't For The 'Ouses In Between*), Charles Wilmott (*In The Twi-Twi-Twilight*) and Fred Leigh, the Literary Editor who wrote the words of *Waiting At The Church*, *Poor John* and *The Galloping Major*. Leslie Stuart worked for Day under contract, writing *Lily Of Laguna*, *Little Dolly Daydream* and *The Soldiers Of The Queen*. Although no formal contract ever existed between them, all of Harry Lauder's songs were published by F, D & H (Harry Lauder was not above popping into the office and buying a parcel of his songs for a couple of bob, to be sold at a respectable profit later).

Every day in the professional department, in and around the 'governor's' office, there were meetings of artists, writers and composers. Forty to fifty songs were now published each month, with a really good month yielding eighty or ninety.

The music publishing industry, and composers in particular, owe much to David Day. He introduced the payment of royalties to artists, composers and authors whose earnings had previously been limited to one or two guineas. Thus Charles Coburn, who had purchased *The Man Who Broke The Bank* from Fred Gilbert in 1891 for ten pounds, found it profitable to sell the song to F, D & H for £5 and a royalty, making himself a handsome profit of over £500.

Harry Lauder

The Performing Right Society, of which David Day was one of the founders in 1914, was finally established to collect royalties for the public performance of works of composers, authors and publishers.

Perhaps of more importance to the music publishing industry was David Day's organisation, the Musical Copyright Association. By 1900, piracy of popular songs was well under way with several printers photographing the original copy and running off scores of pirated sheets on a lithographic press.

The MCA organised 'grab and destroy' raids, using ex-policemen to seize the stocks of the illegal copies and leaving the music pirates to complain to the police – if they dared. This led to quite hectic detective work with pirate presses changing their location when the pace became too hot. It was not until 1911, when the Copyright Act was passed which made it a criminal offence to publish copyright music without permission, that the piracy was eventually stamped out.

In 1905 a branch of F, D & H was opened in New York which was to herald an invasion of America by British artists, Vesta Victoria, Marie Lloyd and Harry Lauder among them. The Americans, who hitherto had plenty of their own material to propagate without paying much attention to the British, returned the compliment, giving us *Ta-Ra-Ra-Boom-De-Ay* and *After The Ball*.

But the Americans had something else to give to the British, the most widespread and violent change ever to take place in popular music in this century – Ragtime!

Harry Tate   *Little Tich*

WON'T YOU BUY MY PRETTY FLOWERS,

NEW BALLAD,

WRITTEN BY   COMPOSED BY

A.W. FRENCH.   &   G.W. PERSLEY.

Sung by GEORGE CLARE of the

MOHAWK MINSTRELS,

AGRICULTURAL HALL, ISLINGTON.

LONDON.
FRANCIS, DAY & HUNTER, 142, CHARING CROSS ROAD (OXFORD ST END.)
PUBLISHERS OF
SMALLWOOD'S CELEBRATED PIANOFORTE TUTOR.

PRICE 3/-
BAND PARTS (for 1st & 2nd Violin
Flute Cornet & Bass complete) 2/6 net
SINGLE PARTS 9d EACH

COPYRIGHT

"WON'T YOU BUY MY PRETTY FLOWERS."

1.

Underneath the gaslight's glitter,
Stands a little fragile girl,
Heedless of the night winds bitter,
As they round about her whirl,
While the hundreds pass unheeding,
In the evening's waning hours,
Still she cries with tearful pleading,
Won't you buy my pretty flow'rs?

REFRAIN

There are many sad and weary,
In this pleasant world of ours,
Crying ev'ry night so dreary,
Won't you buy my pretty flow'rs?

2.

Ever coming, ever going,
Men and women hurry by,
Heedless of the teardrops gleaming.
In her sad and wistful eye,
How her little heart is sighing,
In the cold and dreary hours,
Only listen to her crying,
Won't you buy my pretty flow'rs?

REFRAIN

There are many sad and weary
In this pleasant world of ours,
Crying ev'ry night so dreary,
Won't you buy my pretty flow'rs?

3.

Not a loving word to cheer her,
From the passers by is heard,
Not a friend to linger near her,
With a heart by pity stirr'd,
Homeward goes the tide of fashion,
Seeking pleasure's pleasant bow'rs,
None to hear with sad compassion,
Won't you buy my pretty flow'rs?

REFRAIN

There are many sad and weary,
In this pleasant world of ours,
Crying ev'ry night so dreary,
Won't you buy my pretty flow'rs?

REFRAIN

FRANCIS & DAY'S
❈ NEWEST COMIC SONGS. ❈
Price Two Shillings nett Each.

SUNG BY

Ta-ra-ra-boom-der-é	EVERYBODY
McFadden learning to Waltz...	JOHNNY DANVERS
Bye-and-bye	FARRELL & WILLMOT
Miner's Dream of Home	LEO DRYDEN
Regent Street	CHAS. GODFREY
Scraps from Popular Songs ...	ARTHUR RIGBY
Irishman's Home, sweet Home	J. W. ROWLEY
Good old Annual!	HARRY RANDALL
Girls have the best of it	HARRY LESTER
Not one!	GEO. FAIRBURN
Don't they love us!	WILL BINT
Keep away!	MISS PEARL PENROSE
Dear old Friendly Faces	WALTER STOCKWELL
Lost and Found ...	EVERYBODY
I was surprised ...	J. W. HALL
Johnny, get a Van	CHAS. GARDENER
Something occurred	HARRY RANDALL
That is love (parody)	G. W. HUNTER
Did he get there ?	G. W. HUNTER
Turn it up, tiddly um	W. BINT
Shipmates and messmates	MISS PEARL PENROSE
See him at home...	ALEC HURLEY
Where one goes, we all go	ARTHUR ALBERT
The old house at home...	C. J. McCONNELL
Mary's cheeks are rosy...	MISS PEARL PENROSE
The way to live	HARRY ANDERSON
Welcome the exile home	TOM CARNEY
Puzzling proverbs...	FRANK COYNE
The Temperance Brigade	TOM COSTELLO
It may be so	ARTHUR W. RIGBY
Kate O'Grady	TOM CARNEY
On principle!	ALFRED W. FRENCH
Theosophee...	TOM COSTELLO
So do I, ha! ha! ha!	GEO. FAIRBURN
Right behind!	HARRY RANDALL
As the church bells chime	CHAS. CHAPLIN
Here's my love to ould Ireland	MISS KATE CARNEY
Solomon Levi	FRED. SEAVER
Monday was the day	MISS JENNY HILL
To-morrow ...	CHAS. ROSS
East and West	MISS MARIE LE BLANC
I remember...	G. W. HUNTER
Too-roo-loor-lay	W. F. MOSS
So mote it be	JOLLY JOHN NASH
Johnnie is an angel now	MISS NELLIE L'ESTRANGE
It's only artificial after all	ARTHUR FORREST
Boys of the Royal Navee	MISS NELLIE WILSON
Good health, old boy	HARRY ANDERSON
Whoi-a! wot-o!	McCALL CHAMBERS
How to sing extempore...	GEORGE NENO
Drink, boys, and pass round the wine	GEORGE NENO
The undertaker's man	HARRY ANDLEY
A new hat now	J. C. HEFFRON
I've turned against it now	GEO. BROOKS
A sadder but a wiser man	CHAS. E. NOTT
Maggie Murphy's flat	G. W. HUNTER
My moke	McCALL CHAMBERS
We'd never met before	McCALL CHAMBERS
Sitting down to tea	G. W. HUNTER
That's where the trouble begins	W. F. MOSS

SUNG BY

Now he's climbing up the golden stairs	WALLIS & LANGTON
Just because she didn't know the way	FLORRIE HASTINGS
She danced ...	BOB RAE
To-day I've made sweet Annie Rooney my wife...	MICHAEL NOLAN
A silent maiden ...	CHARLES COBORN
Where have the girls all gone to ?...	WALTER STOCKWELL
We were lads together...	J. W. HALL AND N. C. BOSTOCK
I was underneath...	HARRY LESTER
The girl next door to me	J. W. HALL
Oh, Polly! pretty little Polly!...	ALEC HURLEY
Imagine it ...	BOB RAE
Me and my old pal Brown	ARTHUR FORREST
All doing a little bit	J. W. HALL
Did I go	LESTER BARRETT
Grandad's tales of glory	ELLA DEAN
Danny McCall	ROSE SULLIVAN
They all came back	LESTER BARRETT
Relations	W. F. MOSS
Next Sunday morn	MICHAEL NOLAN
Mine did	SWEENEY & RYLAND
Maggie Murphy's home...	JENNY HILL
Our wedding jubilee	J. W. ROWLEY
Come along, boys	LESTER BARRETT
Down by the sea ..	LESTER BARRETT
Time to put the right foot down	PAUL PELHAM
Truly rural...	CHAS. COBORN
Three mothers-in-law	PAT RAFFERTY
They're all good ...	J. W. ROWLEY
Oh! Billy Cumming, can it really be the truth?	GEO. BEAUCHAMP
Gay Paree ...	CHAS. GODFREY
I felt that I was justified in doing it ...	CHAS. COLLETTE
The grand old British Lion	HARRIETT VERNON
'Twas just down Chelsea way	CHAS. GODFREY
The scandals are "Cumming"	PAUL PELHAM
Two strings to your bow ...	HARRIETT VERNON
The Naval Exhibition ...	GEO. BEAUCHAMP
I went out on strike this morning...	PAT RAFFERTY
Norah, my village queen	PAT RAFFERTY
The Society actor	TOM COSTELLO
Dear old pals of mine ...	FRED. HANLAN
Oh! the models ...	HARRY RANDALL
Her Father's boot	JOHNNY DANVERS
It's all over...	GEO. BEAUCHAMP
The legend of Champagne ...	HARRIETT VERNON
Cleopatra ...	HARRIETT VERNON
Oh! mother-in-law	FELICITAS
First, second, and third	G. W. KENWAY
Let's have another	JESSIE DE GREY
You, and I, and all of us ...	WALTER MUNROE
Fellows we met at the races	J. C. RICE
Three a penny ...	J. C. RICE
He was whistling this tune all day...	LOTTIE COLLINS
Isn't that a dainty dish ?	G. H. MACDERMOTT
Pa and Ma...	G. H. MACDERMOTT
I did laugh ...	HARRY RANDALL
Side by side	ROSE SULLIVAN
Hi! boys, hi! boys, come with your Uncle Joe	VESTA TILLEY
Jolly company	HARRY ANDERSON

FRANCIS, DAY, & HUNTER,
Blenheim House, 195, Oxford Street, London, W.
AND
1 & 3, UNION SQUARE, NEW YORK.
Publishers of SMALLWOOD'S PIANOFORTE TUTOR—the easiest to teach and to learn from. SMALLWOOD'S 55 MELODIOUS EXERCISES, &c.

14

Sung by LEO DRYDEN.

THE MINER'S DREAM OF HOME.

Written and Composed   **WILL GODWIN** and **LEO DRYDEN.**

1.

It is ten weary years since I left England's shore,
  In a far distant Country to roam,
How I long to return to my own Native land—
  To my friends, and the old folks at home!
Last night, as I slumbered, I had a strange dream,
  One that seemed to bring distant friends near,—
I dreamt of Old England, the land of my birth,
  To the heart of her sons ever dear!

REFRAIN.

I saw the old homestead, and faces I love—
  I saw England's valleys and dells;
I listened with joy, as I did when a boy,
  To the sound of the old Village bells.
The log was burning brightly—
  'Twas a night that should banish all sin,
For the bells were ringing the Old Year out,
  And the New Year in!

2.

While the joyous bells rang, swift I wended my way
  To the cot where I lived when a boy;
And I looked in the window— Yes! there, by the fire,
  Sat my parents!— my heart filled with joy.
The tears trickled fast down my bronzed, furrowed cheek,
  As I gazed on my Mother so dear,
I knew in my heart she was raising a pray'r
  For the boy whom she dreamt not was near!
    (*Refrain.*)— I saw the old homestead, &c.

3.

At the door of the cottage we met face to face—
  'Twas the first time for ten weary years;
Soon the past was forgotten— we stood hand-in-hand—
  Father, Mother, and Wand'rer in tears!
Once more in the fire-place the oak log burns bright,
  And I promised no more would I roam;
As I sat in the old vacant chair by the hearth,
  And I sang the dear song— "Home, sweet, Home!"
    (*Refrain.*)— I saw the old homestead, &c.

16

F & D. 3158.

IF IT WASN'T FOR THE 'OUSES IN BETWEEN;
Or, The Cockney's Garden.

WRITTEN BY EDGAR BATEMAN.

COMPOSED BY GEO. LE BRUNN.

18

tur - nip tops and cab - ba - ges wot peo - ple does-n't buy
time the blooming clock strikes there's a cuc - koo sings to me,
dog's 'ouse on the line-post there was pi - geons nine or ten,
mush - rooms in the dust hole, with the cow - cum - bers so green—

I makes it on a Sun - day look all
And I've paint - ed up " To Leath - er Lane a
Till some - one took a brick and knock'd it
It on - ly wants a bit o' 'ot - 'ouse

gay.   The neigh - bours finks I grows 'em and you'd fan - cy you're in Kent,   Or at
mile."   Wiv tom - ar - toes and wiv rad - ish - es wot 'ad - n't a - ny sale,   The
off.   The dust - cart tho' it sel - dom comes, is just like 'ar - vest 'ome   And we
glass.   I wears this milk - man's night - shirt, and I sits out - side all day,   Like the

Ep - som if you gaze in - to the mews—   It's a won - der as the land - lord does - n't
back - yard looks a puf - fick mass o' bloom;   And I've made a lit - tle bee - hive wiv some
mean to rig a dai - ry up some - 'ow—   Put the don - key in the wash-house wiv some
plough - boy cove what's miz-zled o'er the Lea;   And when I goes in-doors at night they

want to raise the rent,   Be - cause we've got such nob - by dis - tant views.
bee - tles in a pail,   And a pitch - fork wiv the han - dle of a broom.
im - i - ta - tion 'orns,   For we're teach - ing 'im to moo just like a kah (cow).
dun - no what I say.   'Cause my lan - guage gets as yo - kel as can be.

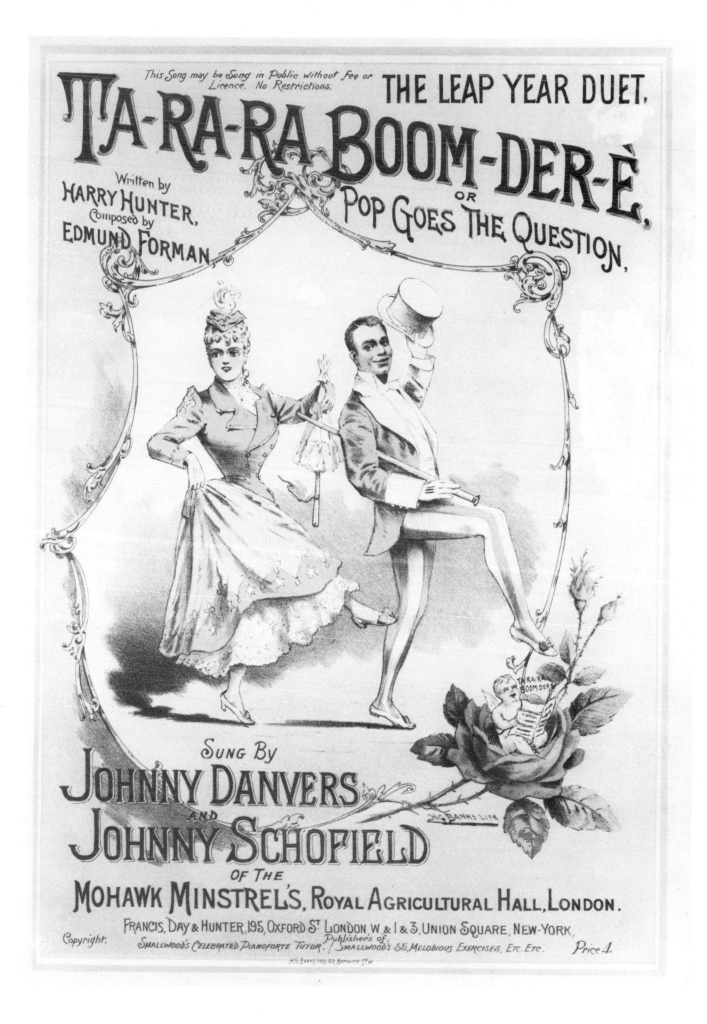

TA-RA-RA, BOOM-DER-È.

HE: My dear Miss Brown I've just call'd in

SHE: And I am just call'd out

HE: Not out of temper Miss I hope,

SHE: Oh, dear no! Can you doubt?
I'm always glad to see you dear,
Of course you know it is Leap Year,
And I can speak with candour,
And be as bold as Alexander!

HE: Well! I'll be bold, then, after that,
And ask you for five minutes chat.

SHE: Ah! That reminds me, my dear John,

HE: Oh! This is nice, love, do go on.

SHE: There is a question I would ask,
But don't know how to do it,

HE: Then I'll assist you in the task,
If you choose to pursue it.

SHE: I hope you will not think me rude,

HE: I'm sure I don't know why I 'shude',

SHE: You will not think me fast, I trust,

HE: Not fast or loose, but lively just.
Oh! I know what she's going to do,
Her love will be unmask'd,
She's going to pop the question,
And I'm waiting to be asked,
I'm waiting, waiting, waiting,
I'm waiting to be asked.
She will declare her passion,
For it's Leap Year and the fashion,
And I'm waiting, waiting, waiting,
I'm waiting to be asked.

SHE: Then I'll ask without more delay,
What is it folks mean when they say,
Ta-ra-ra! Ta-ra-ra? Ta-ra-ra! Boom-der-è!

HE: I think the meaning's very clear,
And this is what it means, my dear,
Ta-ra-ra boom-der-è. Ta-ra-ra Boom-der-è.

SHE: Ta-ra-ra boom-der-è?

HE: Ta-ra-ra boom-der-è!

SHE: Ta-ra-ra boom-der-è?

HE: Ta-ra-ra boom-der-è!

SHE: Ta-ra-ra boom-der-è?

HE: Ta-ra-ra boom-der-è!

BOTH: Ta-ra-ra boom-der-è?

HE: My dear I've quite enjoyed the dance,
But hoped for quite another chance,
It's Leap Year don't you recollect?
Your question was not quite correct!

SHE: What did you think, then, I should do?
What did you think I'd ask of you?

HE: I thought your question, dear, would be,
Will you, will you, marry me?
Leap Year dear and that is when,
Pardon my suggestion,
The ladies court the gentlemen
And pop goes the question!
And I'm waiting, waiting, waiting,
I'm waiting to be asked,
Come and declare your passion,
For it's Leap Year and the fashion,
And I'm waiting, waiting, waiting,
I'm waiting to be asked.

SHE: Then if you're waiting, sir, for me
You'll wait till all eternity,
I never could do it, I'm sure I could never,
I'd rather be single for ever and ever
And you've completely lost your wits,
Pardon my suggestion,
When you say ladies court the men,
And "pop goes the question".

HE: Well! Will you do it just for fun,
Just to oblige a friend,
Do as we oft before have done,
When children let's pretend.

SHE: Well, I don't mind then just for fun,
But how's the game to be begun?

HE: Oh! You must say I'm sweet as honey,
And you don't love me for my money,
Then we'll both look stupid, funny,
Then we will yum! yum! yum!

SHE: Here goes then, dear! Your sweet
complexion,
So fair, so rare, so near perfection,
Has robbed me of my heart's affection,
Then come, my darling come!
Ah yes, indeed, our bliss shall be,
Complete, complete, and never ending,
If you will only come to me,
Remember I am but pretending,
But just in jest I sing to thee,
Will you, will you, marry me?

BOTH: Oh, We've completely lost our wits,
Pardon the suggestion
But in Leap Year the girls are queer,
And pop goes the question

HE: Now on your bosom I must fall,
And weep tears of joy

SHE: You are indeed, my all in all,
My love! My precious, precious boy!
I've loved and long'd for weary years,
If my love thou returnest,
Kiss me, my love, and dry your tears,
Stand back, I'm not in earnest!
But just in jest I sing to thee,
Will you, will you, marry me?

HE: Well, Mary, You may ask papa,
And tell him what your prospects are,
But we must have one little kiss,

SHE: Oh no! I've had enough of this,
'Tis time to end this foolish jest,
I've said too much, too much confess'd,
I cannot ask a man to wed,

HE: Then I'll ask you my dear instead,
In earnest dear I sing to thee,
Will you, will you, marry me?
You've only just one word to say,
And that is Ta-ra-ra boom-der-è!

Ta-ra-ra boom-der-è,
Ta-ra-ra boom-der-è
Ta-ra-ra boom-der-è
Ta-ra-ra boom-der-è
Ta-ra-ra boom-der-è,
Ta-ra-ra boom-der-è.
Ta-ra-ra boom-der-è.

Ta-ra-ra Boom der-é! Ta-ra-ra Boom-der-é! Ta-ra-ra Boom-der-é! Ta-ra-ra Boom-der-é!

Ta-ra-ra Boom-der-é! Ta-ra-ra Boom-der-é! Ta-ra-ra Boom-der-é! Ta-ra-ra Boom-der-é!

DANCE.

Repeat. Fine.

D.C.

F & D. 3262.

"FLORODORA."

A Musical Comedy.

Book by OWEN HALL. **Music by LESLIE STUART.**

Lyrics by E. BOYD=JONES and PAUL RUBENS.

VOCAL MUSIC.

TWO SHILLINGS EACH NET.

SONG—"He loves me, he loves me not"	Miss FLORENCE ST. JOHN
SONG—"The Island of Love"	Miss FLORENCE ST. JOHN
WHISTLING SONG—"Willie was a Gay Boy"	Miss KATE CUTLER
SONG—"I want to be a Military Man"	Mr. LOUIS BRADFIELD
SONG—"The Queen of the Philippine Islands" (In F and G)	Miss EVIE GREENE
SONG—"The Silver Star of Love"	Miss EVIE GREENE
SONG—"When I leave Town"	Miss ADA REEVE
SONG—"Tact"	Miss ADA REEVE
SONG—"I've an Inkling"	Miss ADA REEVE
WHISTLING SONG	Miss KATE CUTLER
SONG—"The Fellow who Might"	Miss KATE CUTLER
SONG—"The Shade of the Palm"	Mr. SYDNEY BARRACLOUGH
SONG—"Land of my Home"	Mr. SYDNEY BARRACLOUGH
SONG—"He didn't like the look of it at all"	Mr. LOUIS BRADFIELD
SONG—"The Millionaire"	Mr. LOUIS BRADFIELD
SONG—"Phrenology"	Mr. CHARLES E. STEVENS
DUET—"Galloping"	Miss KATE CUTLER and Mr. LOUIS BRADFIELD
DUET—"Tell me, pretty Maiden" (I must love some-one)	ENGLISH GIRLS and GILFAIN'S CLERKS

DANCE MUSIC.

TWO SHILLINGS EACH NET.

VALSE	Arranged by CARL KIEFERT
BARN DANCE	Arranged by CARL KIEFERT
LANCERS	Arranged by WARWICK WILLIAMS
QUADRILLES	Arranged by KARL KAPS

PIANOFORTE ARRANGEMENTS.

TWO SHILLINGS EACH NET.

SELECTION	Arranged by ERNEST ALLAN
MARCH	Arranged by WARWICK WILLIAMS

VIOLIN AND PIANOFORTE ARRANGEMENT.

TWO SHILLINGS AND SIXPENCE NET.

SELECTION	Arranged by ERNEST ALLAN

MANDOLINE AND PIANOFORTE ARRANGEMENT.

With 2nd Mandoline, Tenor and Bass Mandola, and Guitar Parts ad lib.

TWO SHILLINGS AND SIXPENCE NET.

SELECTION	Arranged by G. B. MARCHISIO

VOCAL SCORE (*Illustrated*)	net	6 0
Do. do. (Bound in Cloth)	„	8 0
PIANOFORTE	„	3 0
LYRICS	„	0 6

London: FRANCIS, DAY & HUNTER, 142, Charing Cross Rd., W.C.

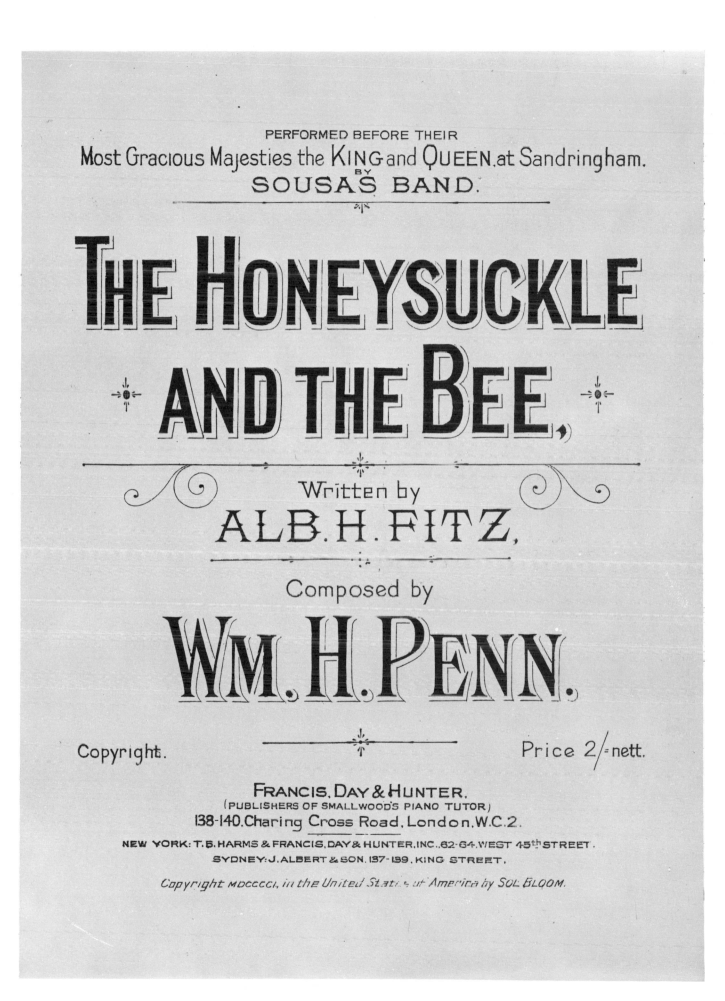

THE HONEYSUCKLE AND THE BEE.

ARRANGED AND SUNG WITH IMMENSE SUCCESS BY CLIFFORD ESSEX.

WRITTEN BY ALB. H. FITZ.

COMPOSED BY Wᵐ. H. PENN.

B'zz .... B'zz.......
1 On a
2. So be_

sum_mer af_ter_noon, Where the hon_ey_suck_les bloom, When all
neath that sky so blue, these two lov_ers fond and true, With their

na_ture seem'd at rest,........ 'Neath a lit_tle rus_tic bow'r, 'Mid the
hearts so filled with bliss;........ As they sat there side by side, He asked

per_fume of the flow'r, A maid_en sat with one she loved the
her to be his bride, She an_swer'd "Yes" and sealed it with a

F & D. ;014.

best............ As they sang the songs of love, From the
kiss;............ For her heart had yield_ed soon, 'Neath the

ar_bour just a_bove, Came a bee which lit up_on the
hon_ey_suck_le's bloom, And thro' life they'd wan_der day by

vine;............ As it sipped the hon_ey_dew, They both
day:............ And he vowed, just like the bee, "I will

vow'd they would be true, Then he whisper'd to her words she thought di_vine;........
build a home for thee", And the bee then seem'd to an_swer them and say;........

rit.

F & D. 7014.

CHORUS.
Daintily.

You are my hon _ ey, hon_ey_suck_le, I am the bee, ...

I'd like to sip the hon _ ey sweet from those red lips, you see;........

I love you dear _ ly, dear_ly, and I want you to love me,.............

D.C.

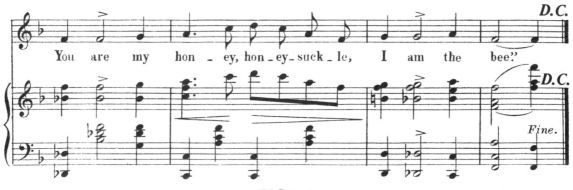

You are my hon _ ey, hon_ey_suck_le, I am the bee."

D.C.

Fine.

F & D. 7014.

Shine On, Harvest Moon.

WRITTEN BY **JACK NORWORTH.**

Composed by **NORA BAYES-NORWORTH.**

COPYRIGHT.

PRICE 2/= NET.

The Theatrical and Music Hall Singing Rights of this Song are Reserved.
For Permissions apply to Francis, Day & Hunter.

LONDON:
FRANCIS, DAY & HUNTER,
142, CHARING CROSS ROAD, W.C.

NEW YORK:
JEROME H. REMICK & Cº
141, WEST 41ST STREET.

Shine On, Harvest Moon.

Written by JACK NORWORTH.

Composed by NORA BAYES-NORWORTH.

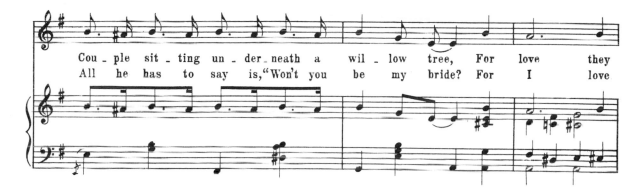

Cou _ ple sit _ ting un _ der _ neath a wil _ low tree, For love they
All he has to say is, "Won't you be my bride? For I love

pine, _____ Lit _ tle maid was most a _ fraid of dark _ ness, So she
you. _____ Why should I be tell _ ing you this se _ cret When I

said, _____ "I guess I'll go." Boy be _ gan to sigh,
know _____ that you can guess? Har _ vest moon will smile,

Looked up at the sky, Told the moon his lit _ tle tale of woe. _____
Shine on all the while, If the lit _ tle girl should an _ swer "Yes." _____

F. & D. 11091.

CHORUS. *2nd time f.*

"Oh! shine on, shine on har_vest moon____ up in the sky.____

I _____ ain't had no lov_in' Since A____pril,__ Jan_u_a_ry, June or Ju_ly.

Snow _ time ain't no time to stay____ out_doors and spoon,____ So,

shine on, shine on, har_vest moon, For me and my gal." "Oh! gal."____

Fine.

D.C.

F & D. 11091.

Printed by HENDERSON & SPALDING, Sylvan Grove, Old Kent Road, S.E.

Bo2 1110

Francis, Day & Hunter
Reg.n. No. 257,748.
Sixpence Nett.

Nº 693. SIXPENNY POPULAR EDITION. (NO DISCOUNT ALLOWED)

This Song may be Sung in Public without Fee or License, except at Theatres and Music Halls, which Rights are Reserved, but may be arranged for on application to FRANCIS, DAY & HUNTER.

"I'M HENERY THE EIGHTH, I AM!"

Written & Composed By

MURRAY & WESTON.

Sung By

HARRY CHAMPION.

Copyright.

London:
FRANCIS, DAY & HUNTER.
142, Charing Cross Road & 22, Denmark Street, W.C.
New York: T.B. HARMS & FRANCIS, DAY & HUNTER, INC., 62-64, West 45th Street.

Copyright MCMXI, in the United States of America by Francis, Day & Hunter.

"I'm Henery the Eighth, I am!"

1.

You don't know who you're looking at; now have a look at me!
I'm a bit of a nob, I am—belong to royal*tee*.
   I'll tell you how it came about; I married Widow Burch,
   And I was King of England when I toddled out of church.
Outside the people started shouting, "Hiphooray!"
Said I, "Get down upon your knees, it's Coronation Day!"

   "I'm Henery the Eighth, I am!
     Henery the Eighth, I am! I am!
  I got married to the widow next door,
    She's been married seven times before.
   Ev'ry one was a Henery—
     she wouldn't have a Willie or a Sam.
  I'm her eighth old man nam'd Henery
    I'm Henery the Eighth, I am!"

2.

I left the 'Duke of Cumberland', a pub up in the town.
Soon, with one or two moochers I was holding up the 'Crown'.
   I sat upon the bucket that the carmen think they own;
   Surrounded by my subjects, I was sitting on the throne.
Out came the potman, saying, "Go on, home to bed!"
Said I, "Now, say another word, and off'll go your head!"

   "I'm Henery the Eighth, I am!
     Henery the Eighth, I am! I am!
  I got married to the widow next door,
    She's been married seven times before.
   Ev'ry one was a Henery—
     she wouldn't have a Willie or a Sam.
  I'm her eighth old man nam'd Henery
    I'm Henery the Eighth, I am!"

3.

Now at a Waxwork Exhibition not so long ago
I was sitting among the kings, I made a lovely show.
   To good old Queen Elizabeth I shouted, "Wot cher, Liz!"
   While people poked my ribs and said, "I wonder who this is!"
One said, "It's Charlie Peace!" and then I got the spike.
I shouted, "Show yer ignorance!" as waxy as you like—

   "I'm Henery the Eighth, I am!
     Henery the Eighth, I am! I am!
  I got married to the widow next door,
    She's been married seven times before.
   Ev'ry one was a Henery—
     she wouldn't have a Willie or a Sam.
  I'm her eighth old man nam'd Henery
    I'm Henery the Eighth, I am!"

4.

The Undertaker called, and to the wife I heard him say,
"Have you got any orders, mum? We're rather slack today!
   I packed up all your other seven for the golden gates;
   Let's have a pound upon account for Henery the Eighth."
But when he measured me with half a yard o' string,
I dropped upon my marrow-bones and sang, "God save the King!"

   "I'm Henery the Eighth, I am!
     Henery the Eighth, I am! I am!
  I got married to the widow next door,
    She's been married seven times before.
   Ev'ry one was a Henery—
     she wouldn't have a Willie or a Sam.
  I'm her eighth old man nam'd Henery
    I'm Henery the Eighth, I am!"

CHORUS. *2nd time* *f.*

"I'm Hen_er_y the Eighth, I am!_____ Hen_er_y the

Eighth, I am! I am!_____ I got mar_ried to the

wid_ow next door, She's been mar_ried sev_en times_____ be_

fore._____ Ev_'ry one was a Hen_er_y_____ she

would_n't have a Wil_lie or a Sam._____ I'm her

eighth old man nam'd Hen_er_y,_____ I'm Hen_er_y the

Eighth, I am!"   am!"

Printed by HENDERSON & SPALDING, Sylvan Grove, Old Kent Road, London, S.E.

Ella Shields

2
RAGS AND RICHES

The opening of the New York office of Francis, Day & Hunter in 1905 was a neat piece of timing. The United States was where it was all happening and the American influence on British popular music was now to remain as a permanent major factor in determining popularity until the mid-Sixties.

The new century was looking for a new style and it was not to be found in Britain. Music Hall and musical comedy happily flowed into the twentieth century with shows like *Floradora* (music by the fore-mentioned Leslie Stuart) achieving continued success from 1900 to 1908. The halls had produced a breed of comedians, Mark Sheridan and Little Tich among them, whose appearance bordered on the grotesque and whose lives, like the tragic clowns they so often were, were disagreeably short. There is something rather neurotic, rather desperate about these comedians to the modern eye; their photographs somehow speak much more of tragedy than comedy.

Another curious product of the halls was the male impersonators, the cigarette-puffing, topper'd and tail'd ladies whose acts, based on the swells of London and the Lion Comiques like Alfred Vance, were widely popular. Vesta Tilley and Ella Shields

"VARIETY'S GARDEN PARTY" AT THE COMMAND PERFORMANCE. *[Hana*

Mr. Harry Claff as " The White Knight," others in the picture being : Martin Adeson, Albert and Edmunds, Charles T. Aldrich, Alexander and Hughes, Athas and Collins, Charles Austin, Wilkie Bard, Edwin Barwick, George Bastow, Beattie and Babs, Clara Bernard, Billie Blnt, Harry Blake, Joe Boganny, Marguerite Broadfoote, Papa Brown, Arthur Carlton, Kate Carney, Dave Carter, Ada Cerito, Harry Champion, G. H. Chirgwin, W. J. Churchill, Paul Cinquevalli, Tom Clare, Charles Coborn, Ida Crispi and Fred Farren, Flora Cromer, Alf. Cruickshank, Fred Curran, Alexandra Dagmar, Herbert Darnley, George D'Albert, Emilie D'Alton, Percy and Harry Delevine, David Devant, R. H. Douglass, Downes and Langford, Duncan and Godfrey, T. E. Dunville, Marriott Edgar, Seth and Albert Egbert, Tom Edwards, Gus Elen, Fred Emney, Edith Evelyn, Fanny Fields, James and Elsie Finney, Ed. E. Ford, Florrie Forde, W. F. Frame, Harry Freeman, George French, Arthur Gallimore, Florrie Gallimore, Barclay Gammon, Harry Grattan, George Gray, Fred Herbert, Diana Hope, Sydney James, James and Will Kellino, Marie Kendall, Fred Kitchen, La Pia, Lupino Lane, Harry Lauder, Mary Law, Albert Le Fre, John Le Hay, Arthur Lennard, Bob and Jennie Lennard, Alfred Lester, George Leyton, Cecilia Loftus, Marie Loftus, Jack Lorimer, Lotto, Lilo and Otto, Sisters Macarte, Jack Marks, Charles and Joe McConnell, Fred and Gus McNaughton, Clarice Mayne and J. W. Tate, Walter Munroe, My Fancy, Newham and Latimar, M. Novikoff, Anna Pavlova, Pipifax and Panlo, Arthur Prince, Peggy Pryde, Harry Randall, Ella Retford, Arthur Rigby, George Robey, Irene Rose, J. W. Rowley, Cliff Ryland, F. V. St. Clair, Ella Shields, Sinclair and Whiteford, Ryder Slone, Florence Smithers, Esta Stella, Stelling and Revell, James Stewart, Tom Stuart, Harry Tate, Joe Tennyson, Little Tich, Vesta Tilley, Alice Tremayne, Dean Tribune, Vasco, Harriet Vernon, Harry Weldon, Horace Wheatley, Charles Whittle, Billy Williams, J. W. Wilson and Nellie Waring, Tom Woottwell.

were the reverse of today's drag acts, obviously satisfying a curiosity in the reversal of sexual roles. A woman smoking or drinking, of course, was deliciously shocking, adding a keen edge to the songs (*I'm Following In Father's Footsteps*, *Burlington Bertie*, etc.) which the performers made famous.

Neither grotesque nor in drag, Marie Lloyd wooed them in the halls with her *risqué* songs, her downright sex appeal and her ability to create an enthusiastic atmosphere. Rejected for being too near the knuckle for the Royal Command Performance of 1912 (Berlin's *Everybody's Doing It* was also withdrawn for the same reason), her absence only marked more strongly the need for her presence.

Her death in 1922 marked the end of the Music Hall era, already declining since 1914 when the London County Council banned drink in the auditorium. The traditions of the era still live on, both in revivals and community songs and in the too often pathetic seaside summer shows. But Music Hall had had a good innings and it was time for something new.

There was no shortage of things new. Blues, rags, jazz, they were new, and they were coming. So was a war which was also to produce its own novel sounds, but it was the syncopated rhythm of ragtime and the flattened 3rd and 7th of the blues which were to make the first invasion.

The truly off-beat rhythm of ragtime had become popular in the States in the 1890s, following the progress of the honky-tonk pianists along the Mississippi and the Missouri. Like most musical styles it was a hybrid, a blend of negro banjo plucking, minstrel harmonies, European polkas and waltzes, and the new rhythm of the cake-walk. A 16-bar theme, a rhythm based on a half-note with syncopation, a regular left hand and an athletic right with just a little improvisation were the ingredients of ragtime.

Scott Joplin's *Maple Leaf Rag* in 1899 was an expression of Joplin's pursuit of ragtime as a form of serious classical music, a pursuit taken up by Jelly Roll Morton and, later, Fats Waller. Ragtime was the forerunner of jazz, giving it a structural harmony and shape.

Irving Berlin

The syncopated frenzy of *Hitchy-Koo* was Tin Pan Alley's version. It was Irving Berlin who popularised the word 'ragtime' with the decidedly non-rags title of *Alexander's Ragtime Band*. This rags-to-riches composer, son of a Russian immigrant, singing waiter and song-plugger from New York's East Side, knew a thing or two about real ragtime – listen to *At The Devil's Ball* – but it was the bugle and trumpet of that band which made the word 'ragtime' famous.

The Original Dixieland Jazz Band, consisting of five white musicians and including among the instruments a trombone, exploded with the *Tiger Rag* and lit the fuse of jazz. George Robey was not alone in condemning jazz as a threat to the sanctity of the family. It had an air of sensuousness, of racy rhythm, it smelt of the brothels of New Orleans from where it was rooted out in 1917. Poured from a potent brew of African Negro, Creole, French and Spanish music, it allowed a great freedom of arrangement based on a regular fundamental beat. As the music followed its black exponents, it became hardened and solidified into the more definite expression of Chicago Jazz but it was Jelly Roll Morton who preserved the lightness and inspiration of classical New Orleans Jazz which, in the 1920s, was gradually substituted for ragtime.

Rags, jazz, what else was new? The Blues. The fundamental mood of the blues is melancholy, a sad chanting of work songs and negro spirituals. William Handy, the Father of the Blues, took his themes from blues performers and turned them into formal harmonisations. The *St Louis Blues* was a blues theme built on to a rags theme, the flattening of the 3rd and 7th, common to most blues, being as near to the imitation of a human voice as an instrument can achieve. The 12-bar blues, as sung and improvised by Bessie Smith, was basically a poem set to music although King Oliver's Band produced a more commercial sound with orchestral improvisation.

Whatever the style of music, however exotic the sound, after 1910 a popular song had to possess a rhythm good enough to dance to. America went dance crazy. The cake-walk, the tango, the fox trot, the bunny hug, the grizzly bear (this one by Irving Berlin and George Botsford): the national mania for speed, to be found in automobiles, aeroplanes and moving pictures, found its way to the dance floor. However unsuitable the song for dancing, an arranger could always be found to produce a dance-floor version. While Shelton Brooks could write a real belter like *Some Of These Days* for that red-hot momma Sophie Tucker, he could also write a real leg-kicker based on an actual event like the *Darktown Strutters Ball* for the Original Dixie-land Jazz Band to popularise.

Not all was rush and bustle. The melodies lingered on, many from the pen of Victor Herbert whose 1910 show of *Naughty Marrietta* kept the ballad popular with *I'm Falling In Love With Someone*, the *Italian Street Song* and *Ah Sweet Mystery Of Life*.

Victor Herbert, one of the first serious composers with a classical music education to apply himself to popular music, founded with George Cohen (composer of *Over There*, the World Wars I and II favourite) the American Society of Composers, Authors and Publishers, the USA equivalent to the British PRS founded that same year.

Perhaps the most significant popular ballad, forerunner of the intimate crooning style which the electric microphones would later permit, was Jerome Kern's *They Didn't Believe Me*. No belting out of this one; a quiet intimacy, not showy or preten-tious but confidential, almost private. Later, in *Oh What A Lovely War*, it was to be given new lyrics by Charles Chilton which lent the song a heartfelt poignancy.

MUSIC AMONG THE RUINS
A Belgian soldier finds solace in his devastated home.

Britain, in the meantime, was slipping, sliding, stumbling into a war which was to have a much more profound effect on her than on the USA. The Music Hall prospered and musical comedies like *The Wizard Of Oz* drew the crowds, with sentimental and romantic operettas following the trail blazed by Gilbert & Sullivan and Johann Strauss. Until the 1914–18 war began, things seemed to be going reasonably smoothly in a pre-ordained world, with hope still in the human breast. There was misery and grime, illness and poverty, but there was also a set order to things, a confidence in a future which would bring the answers.

The World War changed all that, killing off the optimism and leaving in its place a sense of frustration and futility. Perhaps the only good thing to come out of it was the songs which did so much to influence American opinion and persuade the Americans to come in and end the European war.

Felix Powell's *Pack Up Your Troubles* was revived in 1916 by Florrie Forde, a song which showed that the indomitable human spirit would conquer all. Such sentiments died, of course, on the barbed wire and Powell himself committed suicide out of disillusionment when World War II broke out. *Roses Of Picardy*, *The Little Grey Home In The West*, *There's A Long Long Trail* and Novello's *Keep The Home Fires Burning* (sung in harmony with *There's A Long Long Trail* as a Barber Shop Quartet song) all became standards both in Britain and America together with the more light-hearted soldiers' pieces like *Mademoiselle From Armentieres* or *Hinky-Dinky-Parlez-Vous*.

F, D & H were now booming. In the UK, the new Sixpenny Popular Series was doing so well that the old 'pirate' hawkers were recruited to sell the now copyright-protected songs. The hunted and their hunters, to save the embarrassment of remem-bered chases down the Strand, now met in a new branch especially opened for the purpose in Denmark Street. As soon as the new shows like *Chu Chin Chow* hit the theatres, the songs were being hawked around the halls and pubs, and the pianists in the big stores were busy tripping out the notes to encourage sales in all departments.

David Day's son had taken over the thriving US branch and Fred Day, assisted by William Francis Junior, had no easy task on his hands trying to protect copyright in the USA. To avoid niggling restrictions on public performances, many American entertainers would sing British hits in pseudo-Cockney accents, claiming to be singing an impersonation of the song rather than the original.

The founding of ASCAP sorted out these problems and F, D & H were soon to become part of America's over-thriving Tin Pan Alley. Over-thriving because the new media of communications were taking a stealthy, if warm, grip on much of the population. A little winding, an adjustment of the horn, a new needle and in 1918 you could sit back and listen dreamily to Jolson's *Rock-A-Bye Your Baby With A Dixie Melody*. Just a few years later, a turn of a knob could bring you the same voice. The gramophone and radio had arrived.

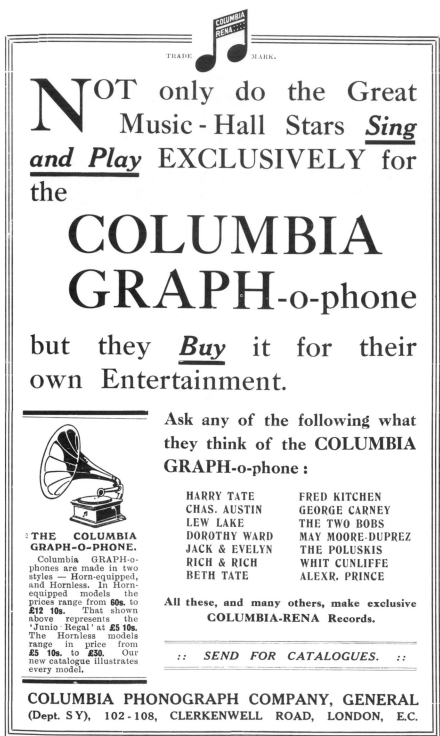

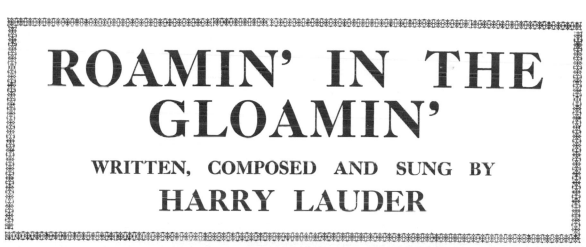

ROAMIN' IN THE GLOAMIN'

WRITTEN, COMPOSED AND SUNG BY
HARRY LAUDER

REPERTOIRE

Bella, the Belle o' Dunoon
It's a Fine Thing to Sing
I love a Lassie   She is ma Daisy
Early in the Morning
Tobermory   Killiecrankie
That's the reason noo I wear a Kilt
Roamin' in the Gloamin'
Wedding o' Sandy McNab
When I get back again tae Bonnie Scotland
Ta-Ta, my Bonnie Maggie Darling
Wee hoose amang the heather
We parted on the Shore
Hey, Donal
The Saftest o' the Family
Stop yer tickling, Jock
Same as his Father did before him
Queen amang the heather
Mr. John McKie
Laddies who fought and won
It's nice to get up in the Morning
My Bonnie, Bonnie Jean
When I was twenty-one
We a' go hame the same way
I wish you were here again
I've loved her ever since she was a Baby
There's somebody waiting for me
I think I'll get wed in the summer-time
O'er the Hill to Ardentinny
Sunshine o' a Bonnie Lass's Smile
Ohio

Copyright 1911 by
Francis, Day & Hunter

Price **2/=** each net

FRANCIS, DAY & HUNTER, 138-140, CHARING CROSS RD LONDON. W.C.2.
PRINTED IN ENGLAND.

ROAMIN' IN THE GLOAMIN'.

Written Composed and Sung by HARRY LAUDER.

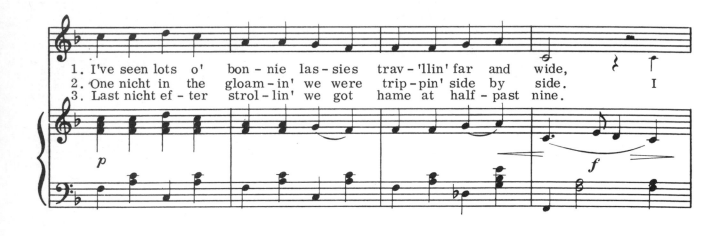

1. I've seen lots o' bon - nie las - sies trav - 'llin' far and wide, I
2. One nicht in the gloam - in' we were trip - pin' side by side.
3. Last nicht ef - ter strol - lin' we got hame at half - past nine.

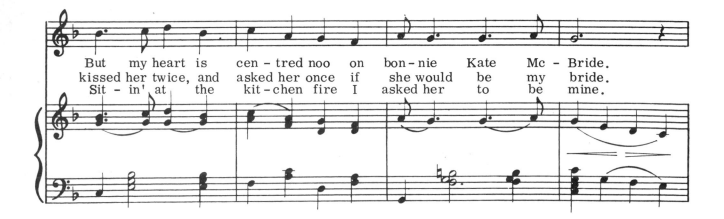

But my heart is cen - tred noo on bon - nie Kate Mc - Bride.
kissed her twice, and asked her once if she would be my bride.
Sit - in' at the kit - chen fire I asked her to be mine.

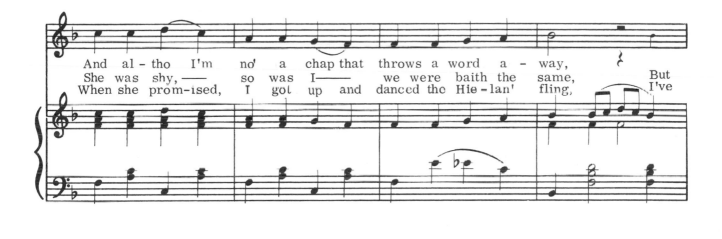

And al - tho I'm no' a chap that throws a word a - way,
She was shy, —— so was I—— we were baith the same,
When she prom - ised, I got up and danced the Hie - lan' fling, But I've

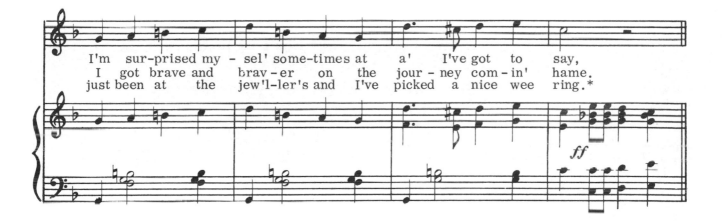

I'm sur - prised my - sel' some - times at a' I've got to say,
I got brave and brav - er on the jour - ney com - in' hame.
just been at the jew'l - ler's and I've picked a nice wee ring.*

*Spoken: Wait till I show you this nice wee ring! (searching pockets). Surely I have'nt lost it!
No! here it is. Man, when I think on sittin' at the fire last night, an listenin' to the kettle singin'-
CHORUS: Roamin' in the Gloamin', etc.

CHORUS *1st time* ***p***, *2nd time* ***f***

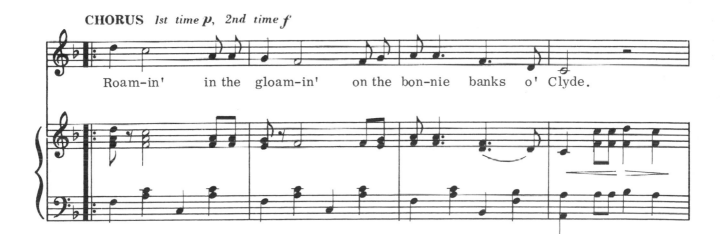

Roam-in' in the gloam-in' on the bon-nie banks o' Clyde.

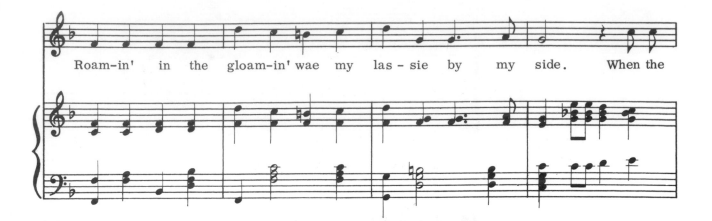

Roam-in' in the gloam-in' wae my las-sie by my side. When the

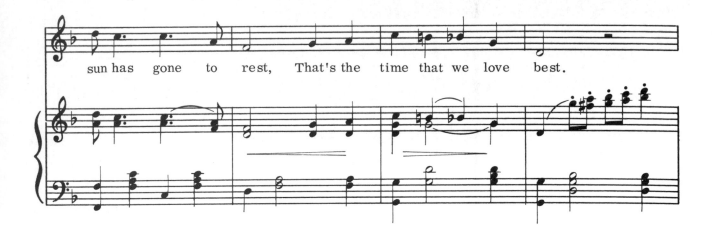

sun has gone to rest, That's the time that we love best.

O, it's love-ly roam-in' in the gloam - - - in'! -in'!

D.C.

Francis, Day & Hunter.
REG⁺ N° 257 148. Sixpence Nett.

N° 946 SIXPENNY POPULAR EDITION. (NO DISCOUNT ALLOWED.)

WAITING FOR THE ROBERT E. LEE.

Written by
L. WOLFE GILBERT.

COMPOSED BY
Lewis F. Muir.

Photo by Hana.

Featured by

THE AMERICAN RAGTIME Octette.

AT THE PIANO

CHARLES S. REID

OTHER SONGS FEATURED by the FAMOUS OCTETTE.
HITCHY KOO.
RAGGING THE BABY TO SLEEP.
THAT HYPNOTIZING MAN.
MY LITTLE LOVIN' SUGAR BABE.

This Song may be Sung in Public without Fee or License, except at Theatres and Music Halls, which Rights are Reserved, but may be Arranged for on Application to Francis, Day & Hunter.

Copyright.

LONDON:
FRANCIS, DAY & HUNTER,
(For all Countries except America, Canada and Australasia.)
142, CHARING CROSS ROAD AND 22, DENMARK STREET, W.C.
NEW YORK:
F. A. MILLS, INC, 122, WEST 36TH STREET.

WAITING FOR THE ROBERT E. LEE.

(Arranged for the Banjo by WALTER REDMOND.)

Written by L. WOLFE GILBERT.

Composed by LEWIS F. MUIR.

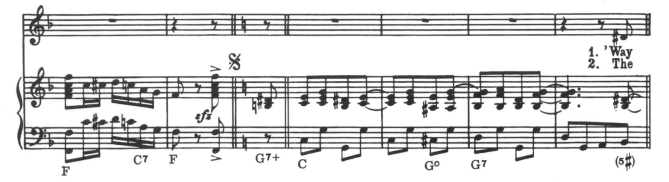

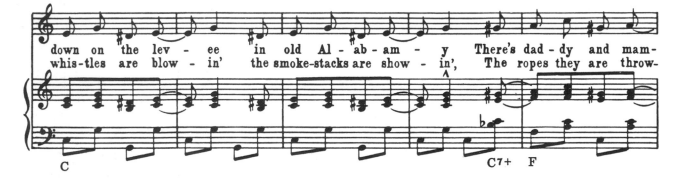

them all. While they are wait - in' the ban-jos are syn - co-pa-tin'.
\- ni - ous, Ev - en the preach - er, he is___ the danc - ing teach-er.

C   D7   G7

What's that they're say - in'?___ What's that they're say - in'___ While they keep play-
Have you been down___ there?___ Were you a - round there? If you ev - er go

C   C7+   F

\- in'___ hum-min' and sway - in'? It's the good   ship
_ there you'll al - ways be found___ there. Why,___ dog   gone!

C7+   F   C   E7

Rob - ert E. Lee___ that's come To car - ry the cot - ton a - way.___
Here comes my ba - by On the good old Rob - ert E. Lee.___

F   C   D7   Fm6   G7   C   G7 C7

Chorus

Watch them shuff-lin' a - long ____ "See them shuff-lin' a - long ____

_ Go take your best gal, real pal, Go down to the lev - ee I

said to the lev - ee And join that shuff - lin' throng ____ Hear that mus-

- ic and song. ____ It's sim-ply great, mate, Wait-in' on the lev-ee,

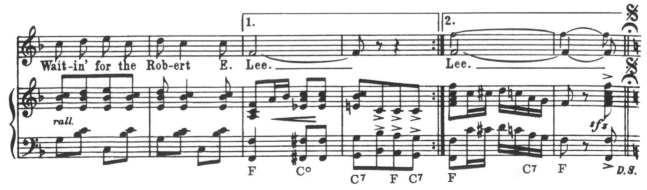

Wait-in' for the Rob-ert E. Lee. ____ Lee. ____

FRANCIS & DAY'S
ALBUM OF BLUES

The St. Louis Blues

Words and Music by
W. C. HANDY

1. I hate to see de ev-'ning sun go down,_____
2. Been to de Gip-sy to get ma for-tune tole,_____
3. You ought to see dat stove pipe brown of mine,_____

F. & D. Ltd. 22685

Feel to-mor-row lak ah feel to day.____
Yas she done tole me, "Don't you wear no black"____
Black-est__ man in__ de whole St. Louis,____

I'll pack my trunk. make ma git a way.____
Go to St. Louis you can win him back."____
Black-er de ber-ry sweet-er are the juice.____

St. Lou-is 'o-man,____ wid her dia-mon' rings,____
Help me to Cai-ro,____ make St. Louis by ma self;____
A-bout a dice game____ he knows a pow'-ful lot,____

Pulls dat man roun'_____ by her ap-ron strings._____
Git to Cai - ro,_____ find ma ole friend Jeff._____
But when work-time comes,_____ he's_____ on de det._____

'Twant for pow - der_____ an' for store-bought hair,_____
Gwine to pin ma - _____ self close to his side,_____
Gwine to ask him_____ for a cold ten - spot_____

De man ah love would not gone no - where._____
If ah flag his train I_____ sho can ride._____
What it takes to git it, he's cer - t'n - ly got._____

F. & D. Ltd. 22685

CHORUS

Got de St. Louis Blues jes_ blue as_ ah_ can be,____
I_ love dat man lak a school-boy_ loves his pie,____

Dat_ man got a heart lak a rock cast in the_ sea,_
Lak a Ken-tuck-y Col -'nel_ loves his_mint an' rye,_

Or_ else he_would-n't_ gone_ so far_ from me.
I'll love ma_ba-by_ till_ de day_ I_ die.

(Spoken) Dog gone it!

F. & D. Ltd. 22685

53

"You made me love you."
(I didn't want to do it.)

Written by
JOE McCARTHY.

Composed by
JAMES V. MONACO.

No. 1047 FRANCIS, DAY & HUNTER'S SIXPENNY EDITION.

Row, Row, Row.

Written by
WILLIAM JEROME.

Composed by
JAMES V. MONACO.

No. 991 FRANCIS, DAY & HUNTER'S SIXPENNY EDITION.

THEY DIDN'T BELIEVE ME.

WORDS BY
M. E. ROURKE.

MUSIC BY
JEROME D. KERN.

Sung by
Adrienne Brune
AND
George Grossmith
IN THE
GEORGE GROSSMITH
AND
J. A. E. MALONE PRODUCTION

"TO-NIGHT'S THE NIGHT,"
at the WINTER GARDEN THEATRE. LONDON.

London: FRANCIS, DAY & HUNTER LTD.
138-140, CHARING CROSS ROAD, W.C.2.

2/-
NET.

THEY DIDN'T BELIEVE ME.

Written by
M. E. ROURKE.

Composed by
JEROME D. KERN.

(He) Got the cut-est lit - tle
(She) Don't know how it hap-pen'd

way,_____ Like to watch you all the day._____
quite,_____ May have been the sum - mer night,_____

And when I told them ___ how beau-ti-ful you are ___
And when I told them ___ how won-der-ful you are ___

___ They did-n't be-lieve me! ___ They did-n't be-lieve me! ___ Your lips, your
___ They did-n't be-lieve me! ___ They did-n't be-lieve me! ___ Your lips, your

eyes, your cheeks, your hair are in a class be-yond com-pare, You're the
eyes, your cur-ly hair are in a class be-yond com-pare, You're the

love-li-est girl ___ that one could see! ___ And when I tell them ___
love-li-est thing ___ that one could see! ___ And when I tell them ___

F. & D. 13835.

F. & D.13835.

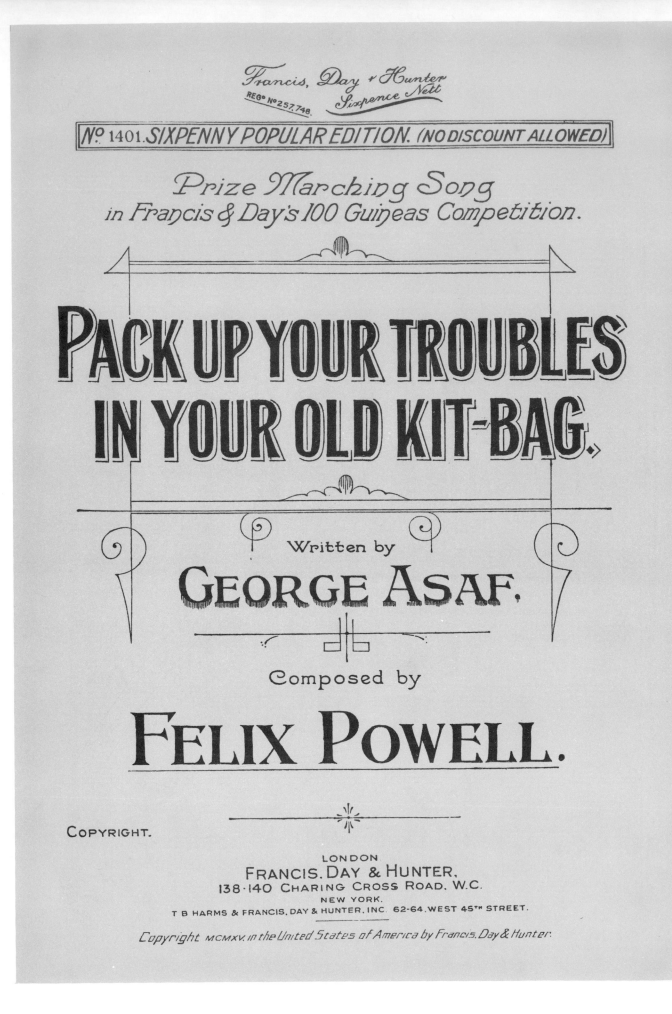

PACK UP YOUR TROUBLES IN YOUR OLD KIT-BAG.

Written by George Asaf

Composed by Felix Powell

F. & D. 14009.

smile._____

smile._____

smile._____

Flush or broke, he'll

When a throng of

He told all his

have his lit - tle joke, He can't be sup - press'd._____

Ger - mans came a - long With a might - y swing,_____

pals, the short, the tall, What a time he'd had;_____

—

—

—

All the oth - er fel - lows have to

Perks yell'd out, "This lit - tle bunch is

And as each en - list - ed like a

grin When he gets this off his chest, (Shout) Hi!

mine! Keep your heads down, boys, and sing (Shout) Hi!

man, Pri - vate Perks said "Now, my lad, Hi!

"Pack up your trou-bles in your old kit - bag, And

smile, smile, smile ⸺ While you've a

lu - ci - fer to light your fag, Smile, boys,

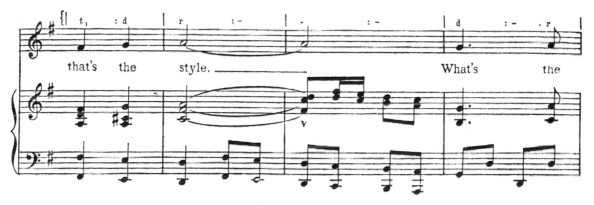

that's the style. ⸺ What's the

use of wor - ry - ing? _____ It nev - er

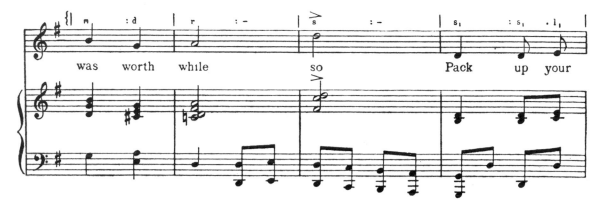

was worth while so Pack up your

trou - bles in your old kit - bag, And smile, smile,

smile." _____   smile." _____

ff

Fine.

D.C.

F.& D.14009.

Printed by HENDERSON & SPALDING, Ltd., Sylvan Grove, Old Kent Road, London, S.E.

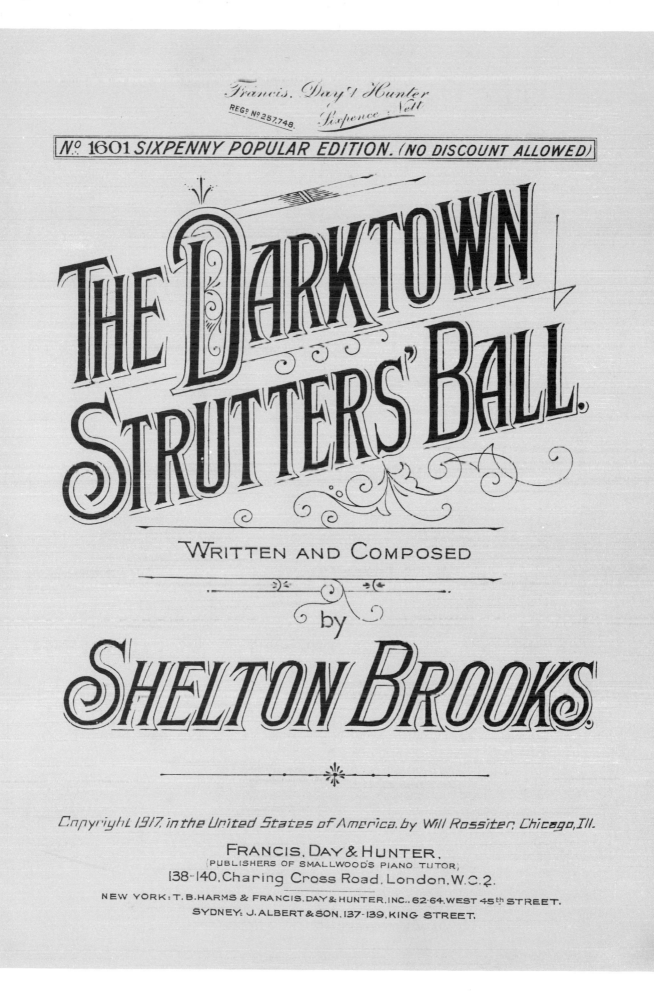

Francis, Day & Hunter

REGᵈ Nᵒ 257,748.   Sixpence Nett

Nᵒ 1601 SIXPENNY POPULAR EDITION. (NO DISCOUNT ALLOWED)

THE DARKTOWN STRUTTERS' BALL.

WRITTEN AND COMPOSED

by

SHELTON BROOKS.

Copyright 1917, in the United States of America, by Will Rossiter, Chicago, Ill.

FRANCIS, DAY & HUNTER.

(PUBLISHERS OF SMALLWOOD'S PIANO TUTOR)

138-140, Charing Cross Road, London, W.C.2.

NEW YORK: T. B. HARMS & FRANCIS, DAY & HUNTER, INC., 62-64, WEST 45th STREET.

SYDNEY: J. ALBERT & SON, 137-139, KING STREET.

The Darktown Strutters' Ball.

Written and Composed by SHELTON BROOKS.

good news, hon - ey, An in - vi - ta - tion to the Dark-town Ball,— It's a
high - ton'd neigh-bours, An ex - hi - bi - tion of the "Ba - by Dolls", And each

1. I've got some
2. We'll meet our

{| t :le .t | t :- :le | t :- | - :t .,t | d' :d' | t :l .s |

ve - ry swell af - fair, _____ All the "high-brows" will be there.
one will do __ their best, _____ Just to out - class all the rest,

{| - :s | l :t | d' :d' | d' :d' .,l | d' t :- .l | - :- | G.t.
r·se,

— I'll wear my high silk hat, and a frock tail coat, __ You
— And there'll be dan - ces from ev - 'ry for - eign land, The

{| l₁ .,se₁ :l₁ .,t₁ | de :t₁ .,l₁ | f .m :- .r | l - :re | m :re | m :re |

wear your Par - is gown, and your new silk shawl, There ain't no doubt a -
class - ic, buck and wing, and the wood - en clog: We'll win that fif - ty

{| m .re :- .m | l - .,m :re .,m | f :f | m .r :- .s | - :- | l - |
f.C.

bout it, babe, We'll be the best dress'd in the hall. _____
dol - lar prize, When we step out and "Walk the Dog." _____

fz

CHORUS. *2nd time*
{:m .,r || d :m | s .,s :l .,s | d' :l | s .m :- .m | r .r :fe .l | l - .,se :l .,t |

I'll be down to get you in a tax - i, hon - ey, You bet - ter be rea - dy a - bout

half past - eight,___ Now, dear - ie, don't be late,___ I want to

be there when the band starts play _ ing, Re - mem - ber when we get there, hon - ey, The

two-steps I'm goin' to have 'em all,___ Goin' to dance out both my shoes___ When they

play the "Jel _ ly Roll Blues"___ To - mor - row night, at the Dark town Strut-ters' Ball.

I'll be

D.C.

F.& D.15029.

BLACK & WHITE.

RAG.

By

GEORGE BOTSFORD.

Copyright.   Price 2/- net

FRANCIS, DAY & HUNTER, 142 CHARING CROSS ROAD, LONDON, W.C.

NEW YORK :- JEROME H. REMICK & Cº, 219-221, WEST 46TH STREET.

Copyright MCMVIII. in the United States of America by JEROME H. REMICK & CO.

Band Journal No. 976.
Full Orchestra 1/6 net.
Septett 1/- ,,
Extra Parts 3d. each.

BLACK AND WHITE.
RAG.

By GEORGE BOTSFORD.

Moderato.

PIANO.

For Permission to reproduce this publication on Mechanical Instruments written application must be made to Francis, Day & Hunter.

F. & D. 12708.

TRIO.

F. & D. 12708.

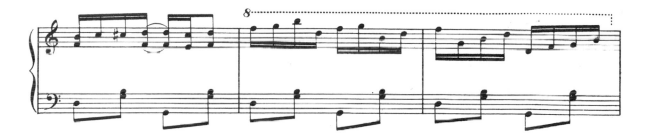

F. & D. 12708.

Printed by HENDERSON & SPALDING, Ltd., Sylvan Grove, Old Kent Road, London, S. E.

Francis, Day & Hunter's
VOCAL SUCCESSES.

	COMPOSED OR SUNG BY
And just then he fell out of bed	Miss Ada Reeve
Archibald, certainly not! ...	George Robey
Artful alliterations	Ben Albert
Black Belle	Miss Amy Clevere
Breakfast in my bed on Sunday morning	Harry Lauder
Brown, broke, and breezy ...	Harry Bedford
By the sea	Carl and Carr
Captain Ginjah, O.T. ...	George Bastow
Come and take tea with me ...	Miss Rose Gower
Come up in my balloon...	... Wilkie Bard
Come with me down Regent Street	
	Miss Daisy James and Miss Winifred Ward
Convict and the bird (The) ...	Tom Costello
Corsican Maid (C and D)...	Miss Evie Greene
Could you tell me? ...	George Robey
Crossed in love was Chrissie ...	Harry Bedford
Dear, kind Poppa	Miss Maidie Scott
Don't do away with the Peers (Piers)	George D'Albert
Don't forget the chorus... ...	Harry Marlow
Don't take me away from the girls	Joe Archer
Doorkeeper at Frightley's (The) ...	Wilkie Bard
Do what you can for ninepence ...	Frank Lynne
Flanagan	Miss Florrie Forde
Fourteen-and-sixpence a week	Jack Pleasants
Gold! Gold! Gold! (Miser's song)	Tom Leamore
Have another one... ...	Chas. R. Whittle
Have you got a cigarette picture?	Bernard Russell
Hear what the crowd say ...	Mark Sheridan
Hermann! Hermann! speak to me in German ...	Miss Vera Saunders
He's a pal	Dan Crawley
He was more like a friend than a husband	Wilkie Bard
Hip-I-addy-I-ay! (Parody) ...	Johnny Danvers
How I climbed the Pole ...	Little Tich
I altered my mind	...Will Bentley
I can see them all to-night ...	Miss Flora Cromer
I do make a hit with the ladies	Miss Hetty King
I don't care if I never get home	Miss Ida Barr
If I'd had my mother there to guide me	Miss Maidie Scott
If the shooting suit should suit	... Wilkie Bard
I keep on walking...	Bernard Russell
I'll be a bad lad, 'Liza Ann! ...	Jack Pleasants
I love to go butterfly-catching	Jack Pleasants
I'm afraid you'll have to come along o'me	Miss Hetty King
I'm Henry the Eighth, I am ...	Harry Champion
I'm setting the village on fire	...Billy Merson
I'm shy, Mary Ellen, I'm shy!	Jack Pleasants
I'm using Sunday language all the week	Harry Randall
I'm waiting here for Kate ...	... Wilkie Bard
Introduce me to the lady ...	Miss Vesta Tilley
I shall sulk	Jack Pleasants
I simply go and do it and it's done ...	George Robey
I suppose she knows	Miss Hetty King
It isn't the Isle of Man any longer ...	Miss Vesta Tilley
It only shows how silly you can be...	Harry Herbert
It's a mad, mad world	Joe Archer
It's so simple!	...Dan Crawley
It's the first time I've been in love	Jack Pleasants
I've got rings on my fingers ("Captain Kidd")	Miss Ellaline Terriss
I've loved her ever since she was a baby	Harry Lauder
I've said good-bye to the dear old Strand	Chas. R. Whittle
I want an idea for a song ...	... Wilkie Bard
I want to sing in Opera	... Wilkie Bard
I wonder what the girls did then	Chas. R. Whittle
Jones	Miss Florrie Gallimore
Just to show who was boss of the house	Jack Pleasants
Keep whistling (Boy Scout song)	Miss Sable Fern

	COMPOSED OR SUNG BY
La-la-la-la, sing this chorus with me	George D'Albert
Let's have a basin of soup ...	Harry Champion
Lighthouse keeper (The) ...	Billy Merson
Lola Lee	Miss Gertie Gitana
Man, man, beautiful man ...	...Will Driscoll
Miss Lollipop	...Miss Eileen Douglas
Mister Owl	...G. H. Elliott
Mother put a card in the window ...	Miss Maidie Scott
Mother's had a row with father	Miss Vesta Victoria
My dear old coat	J. C. Piddock
My inventive kiddie	... Ben Albert
My wife's cake	...Will Bentley
Nature's made a great mistake ...	Gus Elen
Never turn your back upon a fellow	Miss Victoria Monks
Nobody's little daughter ...	... Alec Hurley
Non stops	Ben Albert and Fred Rome
Not a single man said "No" ...	...Wilkie Bard
Now we're civilized	Whit Cunliffe
Oh! blow the scenery on the railway	George Lashwood
Oh, Chantecler	Bernard Russell
Old high hat I got married in (The)	Harry Champion
One of the Deathless Army ...	... Little Tich
Only one girl at a time	George D'Albert
Only think of it (Half a dollar divorce)	... Fred Earle
On Monday I met him	...Tom Costello
On the silvery sands ...	...Miss Madge Temple
Pass along, please!	Arthur Lennard
Picnic; or, Ev'ry laddie loves a lassie	Harry Lauder
Puff! Puff! out went the moon	Miss Millie Hylton
Put on your tat-ta, little girlie ...	Miss Clarice Mayne
Queen amang the heather ...	Harry Lauder
Rip Van Winkle	Miss Florrie Forde
Robin Redbreast	Harry Champion
Sad are the tidings I bring ...	Bernard Russell
Said I—said she	Jack Pleasants
Sam	Miss Helen Trix
Sammy played the Saxophone	Miss Florrie Gallimore
Sea sights (Parody)	... Fred Elton
She'll be seventeen on Sunday	Walter Munroe
Shirts	... Morny Cash
Since poor father joined the Territorials	Billy Williams
South Pole; or, The bounding bounder (The)	Harry Lauder
Sweet Caroline	Miss Gertie Gitana
Take it nice and easy	Chas. R. Whittle
Take your girlie where the band is playing	Miss Maie Ash
There are nice girls everywhere	Whit Cunliffe
There's a little black Cupid in the moon	G. H. Elliott
There's another feller looks like me	George Lashwood
They can't get the better of me	.. Will Bentley
They can't mean what they sing	Edward Kent
They're copper-bottoming them, mum	... Wilkie Bard
'Tis a faded picture	... Frank Cass
Toast those who are absent ...	...Will Godwin
Top o' the mornin', Bridget McCue!	Joe O'Gorman
Verdicts	Bernard Russell
We don't want a girl	Rich and Rich
What would a gentleman do?	...Will Bentley
When father papered the parlour	Billy Williams
When father was mother for a day...	Fred Frampton
When the bugle calls	... Wilkie Bard
Will you sing this glee with me?	... Wilkie Bard
With all my heart (F and A♭) ...	Henry E. Pether
With my little pail and shovel in my hand	W. B. Raby
Wow! wow!	Phil Ray
You are my girlski	... Wilkie Bard
You can't beat London for the girls	Arthur Woodville

London: FRANCIS, DAY & HUNTER, 142, Charing Cross Road, W.C.
New York: T. B. HARMS & FRANCIS, DAY & HUNTER, INC., 1431-3, Broadway.

74

3
OVER THERE AND BACK HERE

Al Jolson

While Britain still struggled with the economic and social problems of the aftermath of the World War, America shrugged off the post-war depression and danced into the lush pastures of the Twenties.

The Jazz Age brought music to the masses. No longer confined to the theatre or the drawing room, popular music was in the streets, in the clubs, the dance halls and in the speakeasies (by 1922 there were 5000 speakeasies in New York alone). In the homes, too: the girls, with short skirts and bobbed hair, no longer worried about being wall-flowers when they could practise dancing to invisible orchestras playing the latest hits on the gramophone and radio. 1920 brought prohibition and women's suffrage, brought cigarette holders, chewing gum and cosmetics. It was the time to fly off at a tangent, to ignore the conventions of the pre-war past.

Production numbers in musical shows dominated popular songs with the *Ziegfeld Follies* and George White's *Scandals* making a regular annual appearance. Despite Ziegfeld's dislike of Eddie Cantor (Ziegfeld himself did not rate very highly in the popularity stakes), the latter was busy turning the *Follies* from musical revues to musical comedy and Fanny Brice was reflecting the spirit of the age with the ambiguous *Secondhand Rose*.

Al Jolson's popularity had yet to reach its height, although he had already recorded George Gershwin's best seller *Swanee*. Composed in 1919 in a quarter of an hour by the nineteen-year-old, handsome, rather vain Gershwin, with lyrics by Irving Caesar, *Swanee* was inseparable from the brash, egotistical personality of the exhibitionist that was Jolson. Showbiz in the Twenties was not for the shy and retiring type, and Jolson was anything but that, selling tickets in the box office for his own show *Bombo* to see how many people were flooding to hear *April Showers*. Irving Berlin's *My Mammy* of 1921 gave Jolson yet another burst of popularity, establishing him as the first of the knee-down, arms-outstretched 'mammy singers'. More of Al Jolson later.

Though musical stage dominated popular song with Irving Berlin, Jerome Kern, Rudolf Friml, Sigmund Romberg, Vincent Youmans and George Gershwin pouring their talents into spectacular shows, jazz had by now invaded vaudeville and, more flagrantly, dance band music. To the Twenties ear, jazz had no clear delineation; it had not acquired the specialist connotations which it has today. It was music to dance to, music with rhythm. Nor was it particularly associated with its negro origins, although its popularity enabled an all-negro cast to achieve success with *Shufflin' Along* in 1921 – from whence came *I'm Just Wild About Harry*. Similarly, in 1923, an all-negro revue *Runnin' Wild* gave birth to the Charleston.

Jazz was essentially regarded as the rhythm of the dance band, and the Big Band Era, with its roots in ragtime and its successor the fox trot, had begun. Dance bands sprouted everywhere, promoted and pushed by radio and records. Already by 1920 *Dardanella* and *The Japanese Sandman* had each sold a million records; it was not until seven years later that a vocal record was to achieve a million sales – Gene Austin's *My Blue Heaven*.

Piano sheet music sales went into decline. Popular songs settled into a standard 32-bar length and arrangers like Arthur Lange could earn $30,000 a year to arrange band parts so that 'the same score sounds equally good on any combination, whether it be a

THE
MELODY MAKER
AND BRITISH METRONOME

*THE only independent Magazine
for all who are directly or
indirectly interested in the
production of Popular Music*

Edited by EDGAR JACKSON

The
" Straight "
v.
" Jazz "
Question

See this page

£100
Competition

2nd
Number

See page 5

Vol. I. No. 4   APRIL, 1926   Price 6d.

A Contemptible Controversy

" The time has come," Doc. Coward   Of ' jazz ' and ' straight,' the saxo-
    said,   phone,
" To talk of many things—   And all the fuss it brings."

(With apologies to Lewis Carroll.)

café band of three or a full symphony orchestra of forty performers. His [Arthur Lange's] name on any band part is sufficient guarantee to all musical directors that the number is OK and that it can be safely performed with the minimum of rehearsing.' (*Melody Maker*, 1926).

Jazz and the dance band cannot be discussed without referring to the 'King of Jazz', Paul Whiteman. Though purists frown at Whiteman's conception of 'symphonic' jazz, he represented the public idea and ideal of the Jazz Age. His version of *Whispering*, which sold over three million copies, earned Whiteman a million dollars. Not a particularly good player himself, his band was technically excellent and he could afford the best players. He set the pace and to imitate him, as Jack Hylton did, was to demonstrate Hylton's good sense.

His concert 'An Experiment in Modern Music' at the Aeolian Hall in New York City, 1924, included Zez Confrey's *Kitten On The Keys*, semi-symphonic arrangements of Irving Berlin compositions, a suite of serenades by Victor Herbert and, most famous of all, George Gershwin's hastily composed *Rhapsody In Blue*, arranged by Ferde Grofe. The same concert in England in 1926 drew slating attacks from the critics, leading the *Melody Maker* to observe: 'It would have been better to have introduced these child-like musical critics into the possibilities of jazz rather through the medium of simpler melodies than through the more extravagant labyrinth of the Gershwin *Rhapsody In Blue*.'

The
" KING OF JAZZ "
Paul Whiteman's Picture at Last

Whiteman had another ace up his sleeve; he had the nascent crooner Bing Crosby as one of The Rhythm Boys, the other two being Al Rinker and Harry Barris. With electrification came the microphone, and with the microphone came a stylised control of the voice. Rudy Vallee, with the aid of a megaphone, already had the intimate style inspired by Whispering Jack Smith, Gene Austen and Art Gilham, but radio and records called for a more polished performance only to be achieved by the microphone. In due course, the microphone appeared in front of the dance band, and the singer, no longer relegated to the back row of the band, became a star feature. Their voices, formerly a mere adjunct to the sound of brass, were now featured with muted backing and the ballad was big business.

Not that the ballad had ever been totally eclipsed. The Jazz Age was also the period of the lush, romantic song, a source of escapism from the hard-boiled post-war blues. The biggest hit show of 1924 was Rudolf Friml's *Rose Marie* in true light-opera style and Vincent Youmans' *No, No Nanette* gave reign for escapism with *I Want To Be Happy* and *Tea For Two* (much as it did when revived in 1972). Irving Berlin abandoned ragtime and comedy for the autobiographical *All Alone* and *What'll I Do*, following these a year later with *Always* and *Remember*. The biggest hit of 1927 was *Ramona* sung by the blonde Mabel Wayne.

from Melody Maker

While the Black Bottom, one of the George White Scandals' eccentric dances, vied with the Charleston for dance floor popularity, Rodgers and Hart slowed down the pace with *Manhattan* and *Sentimental Me*. Sigmund Romberg's *The Desert Song* showed all its European origins in its lyrical romanticism and colourful operatic style.

Gershwin's show *Lady Be Good* gave Fred and Adele Astaire a showcase for their grace and agility as well as giving us the standards *The Man I Love* and *Fascinating Rhythm*. 1927 pushed out the perennial *Showboat* of Hammerstein and Kern and gave Paul Robeson the song which virtually became his by right, *Ol' Man River*. Not a bad list of ballads for an age personified by brashness.

What, meanwhile, of Britain? Slower to recover from a greater involvement in the World War, Britain experienced a time lag behind the popular trends of American music. Music hall still had its far-flung outposts; in 1926 Bud Flanagan, playing the Hippodrome with the inexhaustible Florrie Forde, wrote *Underneath The Arches*, a song that could only be British.

But the insularity of British music could no longer remain immune from American influence and, with a gramophone in most homes, and radio becoming less of a novelty, the barriers fell. Jack Hylton's band was one of the first to become popular via radio with a basically American line-up of wind instruments including four saxophones, two trumpets and Ted Heath on trombone. The BBC had started broadcasting the Savoy Havana Band in 1923, a band with Rudy Vallee as a saxophonist and Billy Mayerl as pianist and composer. As the Savoy Orpheans, the band had weekly broadcasts and by 1925 Henry Hall and Jack Payne were broadcasting regularly. 1926 saw the birth of the first BBC house band, the London Radio Dance Band and in 1928 Jack Payne became the BBC's musical director.

The Savoy Orpheans

*the correspondent in the evening
paper, who, rashly embarking on the
subject of radio dance bands and song
plugging, spoke of:—
" Bundles of pound notes being passed
across to the leader in the restaurant
during broadcasting."*

from Melody Maker

The year 1929 saw a vain attempt by the BBC to stop song-plugging, an established practice of music publishers including Francis, Day and Hunter. Song-plugging both in Britain and the States was considered a normal and essential practice for popularising songs; pluggers were welcome, for example, in silent movie theatres where they led the audiences in choruses of current songs. Band leaders, anxious for radio broadcasts to spread the popularity of their live performances, were not over-paid by the media and welcomed the back-hander which often paid their expenses. While in America bands were keen to find sponsors which would use a popular band to sell their products over the air, in Britain such commercial backing was non-existent (apart from hotels), so a little bribe for a song-plug was more than welcome.

The BBC said stop. It even prevented bands from announcing the titles of songs, until listeners' protests forced the BBC to see sense and raise the ban. Ambrose's band, comfortably installed at the Mayfair hotel where Ambrose received a handsome £10,000 salary, had resisted the ban on such announcements during outside broadcasts, and the BBC, to show no hard feelings, subsequently gave the band the enviable ten-thirty-til-midnight slot on Saturday nights.

Denmark Street in London, where F, D & H's offices were situated just around the corner, was Britain's Tin Pan Alley. It was from here that the few British songs to become world hits made their appearance, most of them from musical comedies. But the USA was calling the tune, most of the tunes, and in 1927 a new sensation appeared in America which Britain, for decades, could not hope to rival.

We're back to Al Jolson. *The Jazz Singer* was a silent film – except for the songs. The talkies, or more appropriately the singies, had arrived courtesy of Warner Brothers. By 1928 *The Singing Fool*, in which Jolson sang *Sonny Boy*, had broken all previous box office records. The first screen musical, *Broadway Melody*, was made in 1929 by MGM (the orchestra actually played on the set) and the first of the Broadway rags-to-riches musical films established the cinema as the main influence on popular music. That year the screen had more popular hits than the stage and by the end of the next decade Hollywood owned most of the world's standard songs.

Music publishers were, by now, not having an easy time. Demand was ever-increasing, fed by radio, records and the talkies, and over-production, too rapid expansion, big turnover and little profit was a cycle which affected F, D & H both in America, whence the hits were mainly coming, and in Britain. Record companies paid negligible royalties on sales – the companies themselves were locked in fierce competition with each other. Fourteen record companies recorded *The Tin Can Fusiliers* before it was arranged and before a band part was published. *The Toy Drum Major* was recorded thirty-two times in one year and *Babette* was done twice on Zonophone, and three times by HMV with Jack Hylton's band, de Groot's Piccadilly Orchestra and Raymond Newton sharing the honours in Britain. Unlike the days of Music Hall, a Tin Pan Alley song was available for any singer or band to present their version and the first record out with a hit stood the best chance of getting good sales.

Sheet music was sold in USA stores at cut prices to attract customers and F, D & H, faced with lean times, merged with T. B. Harms to prevent their being overwhelmed by the frantic pace of the Alley. After the departure of Harms to Chappells, other long-term contracts followed which were to give F, D & H access to an enormous output of hits – contracts with Leo Feist, Robbins, Irving Berlin, Remick Music, Fred Forster, Will Rossiter, Villa Moret, Milton Weil and Handy Brothers. If a song hit escaped the F, D & H catalogue, it wasn't for the want of trying. When David Day died in 1929 he had as a monument to his hard work, skill and enterprise an international company whose catalogue of popular songs spanned every change and fashion in public taste.

1929 was to be a memorable year, appropriately underlined by the St Valentine's Day Massacre. The stock market crashed on Wall Street and it gave a new meaning to the doom-laden word, 'depression'. The lean years had arrived and America, as it had done with music, was to lead the way. The Roaring Twenties went out with a sob. The ball was over.

from Metronome

SWANEE

VOCAL ONE-STEP

Words by I. CAESAR   Music by GEORGE GERSHWIN

SUNG BY

LADDIE CLIFF

IN

ALBERT DE COURVILLE'S

10th LONDON HIPPODROME REVUE

"JIG-SAW!"

FRANCIS, DAY & HUNTER,
PUBLISHERS OF SMALLWOOD'S PIANO TUTOR,
138-140, CHARING CROSS ROAD, LONDON, W.C. 2.
NEW YORK: T. B. HARMS & FRANCIS, DAY & HUNTER, INC., 62-64, WEST 45TH STREET.
SYDNEY: J. ALBERT & SON, 137-139, KING STREET.

SWANEE.

VOCAL ONE-STEP

Words by
I. CAESAR.

Music by
GEORGE GERSHWIN.

The banjos strum-min' soft and low,— I know that you
I'm just a stran-ger 'mid the crowd,— Swan ee, I know

Yearn for me too. Swan ee, You're call-ing me.
I've got to go,— Swan ee. You're call-ing me.

REFRAIN.

Swan ee, how I love you! how I love you! My dear old

Swan ee I'd give the world to be A-mong the folks·

in D-I-X-I E-ven know my Mam my's wait-ing for me,

F. & D. 15407.

REFRAIN.

Swan . . . ee how I love you! how I love you! My dear old

Swan ee I'd give the world to be Among the folks

in D-I-X-I Even know my Mam my's waiting for me,

pray ing for me Down by the Swan ee The folks up north

will see me no more When I go to the Swanee shore.

Fine.

Engraved & Printed by HENDERSON & SPALDING, Ltd., Sylvan Grove, Old Kent Road, London, S.E. 15.

E. & D. 45407.

DON'T BRING LULU.

By BILLY ROSE, LEW BROWN and RAY HENDERSON.

1. "Your pres-ence is re-quest-ed," Wrote lit-tle John-ny White;
2. We all went to the par-ty, A real hi-ton'd af-fair;

"But with this in-vi-ta-tion ___ There is a stip-u-la-tion. When you at-tend this par-ty, You'll
And then a-long came Lu-lu, ___ As wild as an-y Zu-lu; She start-ed in-to shim-my And

all be treat-ed right; But there's a wild and wool-ly wo-man You boys can't in-vite. Now
how the boys did shout, But when she did the hu-la hu-la Then they turn'd her out. Now

CHORUS 2nd time f

"You can bring Pearl, she's a darn nice girl, but don't bring Lu-lu; You can bring Rose with the
"You can bring Nan and bring her old man, but don't bring Lu-lu; You can bring Tess, with her

F. & D. Ltd. 17060.

turn'd up nose, but don't bring Lu-lu. Lu-lu al-ways wants to do What we boys don't
"no" and "yes," but don't bring Lu-lu. Lu-lu has the red-dest hair, Red-der here and

want her to, Ev-'ry-time she starts a-round Lon-don Bridge is fall-ing down. You can bring cake or
red-der there; How can we boys keep our head? Bulls go wild when they see red. You can bring peas and

fil-lets of 'steak, but don't bring Lu-lu; Lu-lu gets blue and she goes 'cuck-oo,' Like the
bis-cuits and cheese, but don't bring Lu-lu; Give her two beers and she bursts in tears And she

clock up-on the shelf. She's the kind of smart-y who breaks up ev-'ry par-ty;
throws cups off the shelf. When she loves with feel-ing, the boys all hit the ceil-ing;

Hull-a-ba-loo-loo, Don't bring Lu-lu, I'll bring her my-self." self."
Hull-a-ba-loo-loo, Don't bring Lu-lu, she'll come by her-self." self."

DC

F. & D. Ltd. 17060.

PRINTED BY UDLOFF & C° LTD

DON'T BRING LULU.

Arrangement for "Banjulele" banjo
and Ukulele by KEL KEECH.

By BILLY ROSE,
LEW BROWN and
RAY HENDERSON.

1. "Your pres-ence is_ re-quest-ed," Wrote lit-tle John-ny White; "But with this in - vi -
2. We all went to_ the par - ty. A real high-ton'd af - fair; And then a - long came

ta - tion_ There is a stip-u - la - tion. When you at-tend this par-ty, You'll all be treat-ed
Lu - lu._ As wild as an - y Zu - lu; She start-ed in_ to shim-my And how the boys did

right; But there's a wild and wool - ly wo - man You boys can't in - vite Now
shout, But when she did the hu - la hu - la Then they turn'd her out Now

CHORUS.

"You can bring Pearl, she's a darn nice girl, but don't bring Lu-lu; You can bring Rose with the
"You can bring Nan and bring her old man, but don't bring Lu-lu; You can bring Tess, with her

turn'd up nose, but don't bring Lu-lu. Lu-lu al-ways wants to do What we boy's don't want her to
"no" and "yes," but don't bring Lu-lu. Lu-lu has the red-dest hair, Red-der here and red-der there;

Ev-'ry-time she starts a-round, Lon-don Bridge is fall-ing down. You can bring cake, or
How can we boys keep our head? Bulls go wild when they see red. You can bring peas and

fil-lets of steak, but don't bring Lu-lu; Lu-lu gets blue and she goes 'cuck-oo', Like the
bis-cuits and cheese, but don't bring Lu-lu; Give her two beers and she bursts in tears And she

clock up - on the shelf. She's the kind of smart-y who breaks up ev-'ry par-ty;
throws cups off the shelf. When she loves with feel-ing, the boys all hit the ceil-ing;

1.
2.

Hull-a - ba-loo-loo, Don't bring Lu'-lu. I'll bring her my - self self._ D.C.
Hull-a - ba-loo-loo, Don't bring Lu-lu. she'll come by her-self. self.'_

When two or more notes are grouped together thus ⁀ they should be stopped by one finger only.
A chord in brackets ( ) may be substituted for the preceding chord at discretion of player.   F & D. Ltd. 17060.

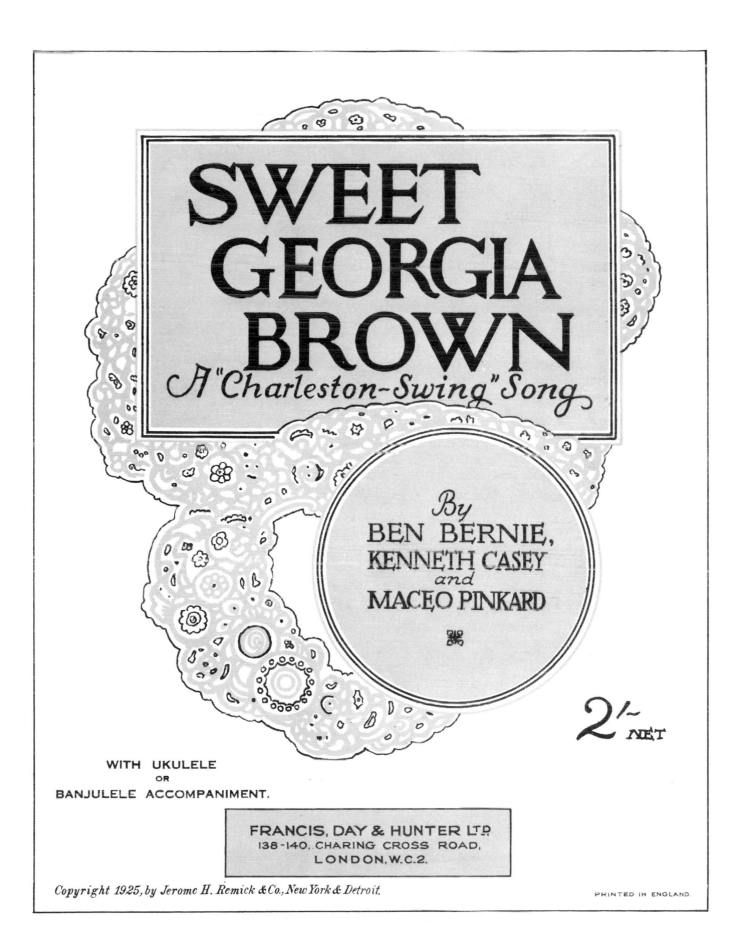

Sweet Georgia Brown.

A "Charleston-Swing" Song.

Tune Ukulele.

A D F# B

Arrangement for "Banjulele" banjo
and Ukulele by KEL KEECH.

By BEN BERNIE, KENNETH CASEY
and MACEO PINKARD.

Moderato.

PIANO.

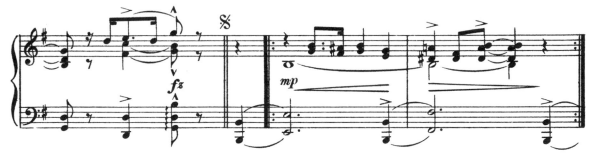

KEY G.

1. She just got here yes-ter-day,—   Things are hot here   now they say;—
2. Brown-skin Gals you'll get the blues   Brown-skin pals you'll sure-ly   lose,—

There's _____ a big change in town, _____
And _____ there's but one ex - cuse; _____

Gals are jeal - ous there's no doubt;   Still the fel - lows rave a - bout ___
Now I've told you who she was ___   And I've told you what she does ___

Sweet _____ sweet Geor - gia Brown; _____ And
Hand _____ this gal her dues; _____ This

ev - er since she came ___   The col - or'd folks all claim, Say
col - or'd maid - en's pray'r ___   Is an - swer'd an - y - where. Say

CHORUS *2nd time f*

No gal made has got the shade On Sweet Geor-gia Brown;

Two left feet, but, oh! so neat has Sweet Geor-gia Brown.—

They all sigh — and wan-na die, For Sweet Geor-gia Brown; I'll tell you just

why, ——— You know I don't lie,

(Spoken ad lib.)

Not much;

It's been said_ she knocks'em dead when she lands in town;_
All those tips_ the por-ter slips to Sweet Geor-gia Brown;

Since she came_ why it's a shame how she cools 'em down._
They buy clothes at fash-ion shows with one dol-lar down._

Fel-lers she can't get_ are fel-lers she ain't met; Geor-gia claimed her,
Oh! Boy, tip your hats; Oh! joy, she's the "cats." Who's that, Mis-ter?

Geor-gia named her Sweet Geor-gia Brown.
'Taint her sis-ter, Sweet Geor-gia Brown.

F.& D.Ltd.17098.

PRINTED BY UDLOFF & Cº LTD

MANHATTAN

Words by
LORENZ HART

Music by
RICHARD RODGERS

F. & D. Ltd. 22455

breez - es blow, To and fro, And tell me what street com - pares with Mott Street
shell-fish grin, Fin to fin, I'd like to take a sail on Ja - mai - ca
kiss we stole, Soul to soul, And South Pa - ci - fic is a ter - ri - fic
great suc - cess, More or less, A short va - ca - tion on In - spir - a - tion

Gm7 C7   Gm   C7 F   D7   Gm   C13 C7

in Ju - ly, _____ Sweet push carts gent - ly glid - ing by. _____
Bay with you, _____ And fair Can - ar - sie's Lakes _____ we'll view _____
show they say, _____ We both may see it close _____ some day _____
Point we'll spend, _____ And in the sta - tion house _____ we'll end _____

F   FO   C7   Gm7   C7   Cm

_ The great big cit - y's a wond-'rous toy, Just made for a girl and boy
_ The cit - y's bus - tle can-not des - troy The dreams of a girl and boy
_ The cit - y's clam-our can nev - er spoil The dreams of a boy and goil
_ But Civ - ic Vir - tue can-not des - troy The dreams of a girl and boy

D7   Gm7   Dm Bb6 Bbm   +6   F   G9

We'll turn Man - hat - tan In - to an isle of joy. _____   joy. _____
We'll turn Man - hat - tan In - to an isle of joy. _____   joy. _____
We'll turn Man - hat - tan In - to an isle of joy. _____   joy. _____
We'll turn Man - hat - tan In - to an isle of joy. _____   joy. _____

f   FO G7   C13   F   FO Gm7 C6 C7   F   Bb F   Fine

F

F. & D. Ltd. 22455

97

INTRODUCTION and VERSE

Sum-mer jour-neys to Ni-ag-ra And to oth-er plac-es ag-gra-

-vate all our cares; We'll save our fares; I've a coz-y lit-tle flat in

what is known as old Man-hat-tan, We'll set-tle down right here in town.

Back to Refrain

F. & D. Ltd. 22455

YES SIR, THAT'S MY BABY.
Song Fox-Trot.

Written by
GUS KAHN.

Tune Ukulele.

Composed by
WALTER DONALDSON.

PIANO.

KEY E♭.

| d' | :d' | l | :l | s | :s | m | :— |

1. Who's that com - ing down the street?
2. Who's the 'who' I rave a - bout?

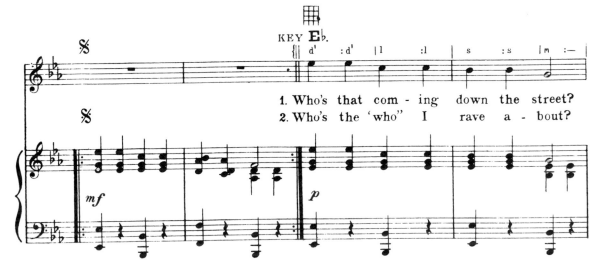

F & D. Ltd. 17120.

PRINTED BY UDLOFF & Cº LTD

CHORUS. *2nd time* *f*

Ra - mon - a, I hear the mis - sion bells a - bove,_____ Ra -

mon - a, they're ring-ing out our song of love._____ I

press you, ca - ress you, and bless the day you taught me to care, To

al - ways re - mem - ber the ramb-ling rose you wear in your hair. Ra -

Dog3031

F.& D. Ltd.18233.

D.C.

HENDERSON & SPALDING LTD.
Music Engravers & Printers, London

Four Successes from "Clowns In Clover."

Little Boy Blues.
FOX-TROT SONG.

Words by
DESMOND CARTER.

Music by
VIVIAN ELLIS.

Copyright 1927, by Francis, Day & Hunter, Ltd.

I'll Say To You.
FOX-TROT SONG.

Words by
CHICK ENDOR.

Music by
EDDIE WARD.

Copyright 1925, by T. B. Harms Co., New York.

There's A Trick In Pickin' A Chick-Chick-Chicken.
FOX-TROT SONG.

Written by
CHARLES TOBIAS and COLEMAN GOETZ.

Composed by
J. RUSSELL ROBINSON.

Copyright 1927, by Leo. Feist, Inc., 231-235, West 40th Street, New York.

On The Wings Of Love.

Words by
DONOVAN PARSONS.

Music by
NOEL GAY.

Copyright 1927, by Francis, Day & Hunter, Ltd.

PRICE 2/- SHILLINGS EACH COPY.

FRANCIS, DAY & HUNTER, Ltd., **138-140**, Charing Cross Road, London. W.C.

108

Me And My Shadow.

Written by
BILLY ROSE.

Tune Ukulele.

Composed by
AL JOLSON and
DAVE DREYER.

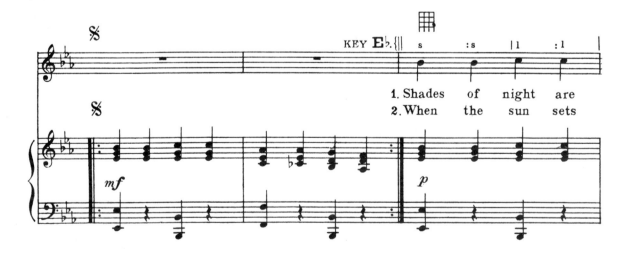

1. Shades of night are
2. When the sun sets

F. & D. Ltd. 17944.

we climb the stair, _We nev-er knock_ _for_

no-bod-y's there; _Just me_ _and my_

shad _ow,_ _All a-lone and feel-ing_

1.

blue.

2.

blue.

D.C.

EB,022628

F:& D. Ltd. 17944.

HENDERSON & SPALDING Lᵗᵒ.
PRINTERS OF BOOKS AND MUSIC LONDON

The Song Is Ended
(But The Melody Lingers On.)
WALTZ SONG.

Written and Composed by
IRVING BERLIN.

Valse moderato.

The song___ is end-ed but the mel-o-dy ling-ers on; You and the song are

What Do We Do On A
Dew-Dew-Dewy Day?
FOX-TROT SONG.

Written and Composed by HOWARD JOHNSON, CHAS. TOBIAS and AL SHERMAN.

Moderato.

All we do is go out walk-ing, when the sun shines bright and gay, But what do we do,

MY BLUE HEAVEN.
FOX-TROT BALLAD.

Written by
GEORGE WHITING.

Composed by
WALTER DONALDSON.

Moderato.

When Whip-poor-wills call___ and ev-'ning is nigh___ I hur-ry to my

DAWNING.
FOX-TROT SONG.

Moderato. Written and Composed by ABNER SILVER and MACEO PINKARD.

Morn-ing glor-ies all tell their stor-ies, at dawn - ing;___ Ev-'ry dais-y just

PRICE TWO SHILLINGS EACH.
FRANCIS, DAY & HUNTER, Ltd., **138-140**, Charing Cross Road, London. W.C. **2**.

114

4
THE LEAN YEARS

The Depression had arrived, but it didn't fall with the abruptness of a curtain after the performance of the Twenties. It was a gradual process of decay. For the poor, it meant becoming poorer, with fewer opportunities for climbing out of the pit. For the majority of the rich, those who resisted the long drop from the top floor, it meant becoming less rich, a slowing down of the pace. For those in between it meant uncertainty and insecurity, a wary determination to hang on to what they had got. For all, it meant a new need for hope, and music – popular music – fulfilled some of that need.

The bands gained strength from the economic weakness, providing escapism on the dance floor and on the radio. They washed the blues away and, for a time, the soul-searching blues went into a popular decline. Though some songs captured the melancholy of the plight of many – *My Forgotten Man, Brother Can You Spare A Dime, Ten Cents A Dance* – tough music with social comment did not provide the kind of relief that most of the public wanted; hot jazz, until the advent of swing, was given less airtime and the popular song was either cheerful, romantic, relaxing or foot-tapping. With the repeal of Prohibition in 1932, the twilight speakeasies yielded up their players (like Jack and Charley Teagarden) to the big commercial bands. In Britain the Ministry of Labour enforced a ban on aliens recording with British bands without special permission and, though Britain may at this time have seemed to be a colony for the promotion of American songs, British bands had little fear of being swamped by their American counterparts. The bands everywhere were growing bigger, their sound growing louder.

The Dorsey Brothers were real jazz guys back in 1919 when this pic was made. That's Tommy and his sliphorn, prone atop the piano. Jimmy is over at the right there wrestling on alto sax. The trumpeter is Soccer Miller. At the piano is Kay Crossan, while Jim Crossan is "floored" by his own fiddling. Beatin' the tubs is Don Nyer. All six hailed from the Pennsylvania coal mine territory and were ready to start out on their own. The Dorseys later gained fame with the Scranton Sirens. Today, Tommy and band are breaking all records at New York's Astor Hotel, while a few blocks south, at the Pennsylvania, Jimmy and gang are doing "biz."

from Downbeat

A public now accustomed to a wide range of music brought to them by live performances, movies, radios and records was a public that was learning discrimination, and the big bands were now relying on the arrangers for the presentation of their sound. In England, Ray Noble joined Lawrence Wright as dance band arranger, moving later to the BBC and ultimately to that musician's goal, the States. Noble's *Love Is The Sweetest Thing*, sung by the ubiquitous Al Bowlly and played by the New Mayfair Dance Orchestra, is Noble at his best and by 1934 Noble's records were selling well in America. By then he had acquired his own arranger, Glenn Miller, whose arrangements for the Dorsey Brothers gave him the basis for his own popularity in the Forties.

Behind the bands of Benny Goodman and Tommy Dorsey were the arrangements of Fletcher Henderson and Sy Oliver. Henderson's band, which boasted the tenor saxophonist Coleman Hawkins, was one of the few negro bands, along with Duke Ellington and Count Basie, which remained popular while securely following the traditions of jazz. His arrangements converted the conventional dance band rhythm into the swing of Benny Goodman and, by 1935, 'Swing was the Thing'. From this point, American bands followed three not always distinct paths – swing, straight and a more closely defined jazz. The straight bands, with exceptions like those of Casa Loma and Isham Jones, were less jazz-influenced and often less versatile. For all that, their popularity – like that of Guy Lombardo's – may not necessarily have been diminished. Though Paul Whiteman was sounding dated by the late Thirties, he never ceased to look for new singers, musicians and song writers (he couldn't have been that dated to be employing the talents of Hoagy Carmichael and Johnny Mercer) and many of his fans remained faithful until he took to the air as a disc jockey.

Whiteman Disbands; Sidemen Seek Jobs

New York—The fate of the Paul Whiteman band hinged on several developments last week. All members of the band were either working with other bands or looking for work, while PW himself stayed at his farm in Stockton, N. J., feeding his cows and pigs and horses.

Frank Burke, personal manager for Whiteman, has left the Whiteman job and the city. It was said Burke would return to Minneapolis and open a publicity office there.

Teagarden in Pit Band

Whiteman's band has scattered, although many of his men were under long contracts. In each case, however, Whiteman had option stipulations, which meant he could fire the men after every 13 weeks, no matter how many years they were signed to him. George Wettling, ace drummer, is working at Nick's in the Village with a band composed of Joe Sullivan, Eddie Condon, Max Kaminsky, Pee-Wee Russell, Al Gold and Artie Shapiro. Artie also was left stranded when Whiteman disbanded.

Bob Alexy joined Larry Clinton, as did Joe Mooney, blind accordionist-arranger. Charlie Teagarden is working in the pit band at the Roxy Theater here. Mike Pingitore, Goldie and others long associated with Whiteman are not working anywhere. Nat Lobovsky, trombone, joined Jimmy Dorsey.

from Downbeat

Movie Work Finished

The Ritz-Carlton job in Boston was cancelled long ago. Whiteman still has several state fairs to play in August and September.

Whiteman recently finished work in a movie on the coast which stars Judy Garland. Teagarden, Pingitore, Goldie and two others from the band worked with PW on the film. Ironical part of the split is that *Down Beat*, which has been carrying Warren Scholl's vivid story of the Whiteman band since its inception in 1919—a story which started March 15 and has run every issue since—ends the series in this issue just as the great Whiteman crew comes to the end of the road, at least for the time being.

The most creative bands, whose sound most closely approximated the conception of true jazz, tended to be black. Although the white bands of Benny Goodman, the xylophonist Red Norvo and Charlie Barnet could compete with the best of them, it was negro music which favoured the purer forms of jazz. Duke Ellington, whose Broadway debut was in Gershwin's 1929 *Liza*, specialised in improvising soloists. In 1934 Ellington's *Solitude* won the ASCAP award of $2500 for the best popular song of the year. Count Basie's Orchestra, with Basie as pianist, brought a new aspect to improvisation with Basie dropping timekeeping in his left hand on all beats. Louis Armstrong was already established by the late Twenties as a virtuoso trumpet soloist, and the bands of Cab Calloway, Jimmie Lunceford and Lionel Hampton kept negro jazz developing as a creative art without resorting to the banality demanded by commercialization.

Not that commercialization always had to be banal. Nor was swing to be decried because it had mass appeal. At their height, in the early Forties, the swing bands included players whose technical accomplishments were unequalled.

Basically, the swing sound was composed of three sections, trumpets, trombones and saxophones, with the baritone sax adding 'bottom' to the reed section in the Forties. Benny Goodman, that King of Swing whose recording of Mozart's Clarinet Concerto was one in the eye for devotees of solely classical music, had them jiving in the aisles of Carnegie Hall and the Paramount Theatre in 1938. His band included

Duke Says Swing Is Stagnant!

But Noted Negro Leader, Composer And Pianist Believes Future Bright If Musicians Wake Up and Work

By Duke Ellington

New York—The most significant thing that can be said about swing music today is that it has become stagnant.

Nothing of importance, nothing new, nothing either original or creative has occurred in the swing field during the last two years.

Offers Ironic Twist

It becomes necessary to adopt a far-seeing and mature point of view when considering the current popularity of swing, revising in the mind's eye its inception, the conditions and circumstances surrounding its birth and growth and the completion of the cycle as it appears today. Much has been written about swing, it has been defined 1,999 times and it has been the subject of much controversy.

An ironic twist to the situation has bitten deeply into the minds of many of the actual purveyors of swing music. Those musicians who were "swinging" on their instruments 10 and 15 years ago, (before the appellation "swing" had any significance other than that of inferring in what style the music was to be played), today look on, some with amusement, others with intolerance, at the farce which is being played out to the full on that merry-go-round known as the amusement world.

'Jazz Still Developing'

What is important is the fact that Jazz has something to say. It speaks in many manners, taking always original and authentic form. Still in the throes of development and formation, it has fought its way upwards through the effortful struggles of sincere and irate musicians, has fought to escape mal-judgment at the hands of its own "caucified critics," those fanatical fans who have woven about it interminable toils. It has striven in a world of other values, to get across its own message, and in so doing, is striving toward legitimate acceptance, in proportion to its own merits.

from Downbeat

himself on clarinet, Harry James on trumpet and Gene Krupa – soon to leave to form his own less orthodox band – on drums, the hot improvisation of the soloist and the expectancy of the answering *riff* were trademarks of the commercial swing bands, whose signature tunes alone brought on frenzied applause.

No band, in truth, was entirely devoted to swing though their reputation may have been built on a swing sound. No band, indeed, kept its line-up intact from year to year. Musicians were constantly poached from band to band, singers like Al Bowlly recorded with upwards of a dozen different bands and when a performance was shared, either live or on the radio, the bands would try to outdo each other in repertoire and, often, volume. Tommy Dorsey's band of the Thirties was not that of the Forties; the same was true of Benny Goodman.

Artie Shaw Grabs Goodman's Men

'Did Me a Favor'—Benny; Mayo Operation a Success

By 1940, the Big Band Era was at its peak and the money followed the bands – Benny Goodman having become a dollar millionaire in three years. Throughout the Depression, the bands could fill the halls wherever they went. Although record production dropped from 104 million discs in 1928 to six million in 1932, with a record needing only to sell 10,000 copies to be a hit, radio broadcasts gave the bands the exposure they needed to retain a large and enthusiastic following. In 1940 Bob Crosby's Band made $50,000 although the singer, Doris Day, was taking home only $50 a week. Arty Shaw had given the Swing Era musical respectability by applying swing to the arrangements of works by Jerome Kern and Cole Porter – though not many Broadway composers were ardent fans of such arrangements. The 'straight' bands kept their following, Guy Lombardo playing New York from 1929 to 1962. Leo Reisman's band made the first LP record for RCA Victor in 1931, featuring Fred and Adele Astaire, though Reisman suffered Whiteman's fate of sounding dated by the end of the decade. Isham Jones' band, whose recording of *Wabash Blues* in 1922 sold two million copies, hit with Hoagy Carmichael's *Stardust* in 1930 and continued to play Jones' hit songs, many written with Gus Kahn, throughout the Thirties.

• SIXTH ANNIVERSARY ISSUE •

Petrillo Jerks Bands Off the Air

Down Beat

608 S. Dearborn, Chicago, Illinois

Entered as second class matter October 6, 1939, at the post office at Chicago, Illinois, under the Act of March 3, 1879. Copyright 1940, By Down Beat Publishing Co., Inc.

Subscription prices, $3.00 a year in the United States; $4.50 in Canada (Canadian Dollars) $4.00 elsewhere. Down Beat is published twice-monthly. Printed in U.S.A. Registered U.S. Pat. Office.

VOL. 7, No. 14   CHICAGO, JULY 15, 1940   15 CENTS

New York Chatter—

Dorsey Does Top Biz in 'Big Town'

BY JACK EGAN

With the possible exception of the Hotel New Yorker, which switches bands in the middle of the summer, the hot spell scene for the dance bands around Father Knickerbocker's little playground seems pretty well set. The squawks we mentioned about sad business a couple of columns ago, have eased down, probably because business around the bandstands has improved considerably. The World's Fair has been drawing big crowds eastward, New Yorkers are pointing at other New Yorkers and calling them visiting firemen and visiting firemen aren't pointing at anybody but just go about having a good time and making the finger pointing New Yorkers so much richer.

Tommy Does Best Biz

Top business in town, confirmed by *Variety*, is being done by Tommy Dorsey and his crew at the Hotel Astor Roof. He's not only broken the record for the Roof, but also hit the high one-night attendance draw of any Metropolitan supper room with over 1,100 covers.

Larry Clinton has been a consistent runner-up at the Hotel New Yorker, sharing second-draw honors with Jimmy Dorsey at the (Modulate to Page 10)

Artie and Lana Are Separated

Los Angeles—Artie Shaw and Lana Turner, who were married February 14 of this year, have separated. Differences in "artistic" temperaments was said to have caused the split. On July 3, Lana filed suit for divorce, charging "mental suffering." Shaw was married twice before he took vows with Miss Turner. Shaw did not comment. He has refused to see reporters for several weeks here.

Three On a Toot

Chicago—Cecil Gullickson, Bob McCracken and Eddie Jacobs of the Leonard Keller band, at the Bismarck Hotel here, celebrated the "fourth" their own way. But they haven't nerve enough, yet, to try it on the air. Keller is a click at the spot. *Ray Rising pic.*

Hawkins' Paris Home Bombed

New York — Coleman Hawkins' home in Paris was recently destroyed in a German air raid, Hawkins was informed last week. The residence cost "Bean" some $15,000 a few years ago when he was touring Europe and using Paris as a base from which to operate.

Hawk and his band opened a 12-week date at the Savoy Ballroom July 4. Has three NBC airshots weekly.

Leaves Dooley

Flint, Mich.—Bobbie Todd, former sparrow with Phil Dooley, was with the new Dirk Courtenay band which opened last month at Samoa Gardens here. The band is "strictly commercial," in the leader's own words, and includes 4 saxes, 3 brass and 3 rhythm. Courtenay is a former press agent.

Ella Fitzgerald Mobbed by Crowd; Clothes Ripped Off

New Orleans—More than 4,000 Negroes, hysterical and in a panic mood, tore the clothes off Ella Fitzgerald late last month when she left the stand and made her way to an exit in the New Rhythm Club here following a one-nighter.

Many were knocked down, several were trampled and wild confusion reigned as hundreds of colored dancers rushed the "first lady of swing" for autographs. Police were called and attempted to maintain order. It was one of the largest crowds ever assembled in this city for a "race" dance.

Ella and her band—the old Chick Webb group with a few changes—

Fitzgerald

are touring the south. Ella was uninjured in the rush, but her gown was ripped and she escaped before the crowd could trample her underfoot.

Ink Spot is 'Typical Father'

BY ONAH SPENCER

One of the Four Ink Spots, Orville (Happy) Jones, was awarded a solid gold diaper pin last week for being chosen the "typical Harlem father."

Jones has seven children. A committee from the Harlem Chamber of Commerce made the presentation and a ball was held in Happy's honor at Savoy ballroom.

Tadpoles Become Big Frogs As Pubs Seek MBS Plugs

BY ED FLYNN

New York—Pandemonium reigns along Tune Pan Alley as many of America's greatest dance bands are temporarily not being heard over the mighty NBC and CBS chains on sustainers.

Prexy Petrillo's ban of remote control airshots caused consternation among the tunesmiths, publishers and pluggers. Probably more so than among the leaders and musicians themselves, who knew what Petrillo was doing and were glad to "go along" with him in the hopes his action would settle the St. Paul and Richmond strikes. The ban made Mutual the biggest thing in the business, as far as pluggers were concerned, and small name outfits with Mutual wires, scattered through Jersey and north of the city, suddenly became top names. Songpluggers swarmed upon the few leaders who were still broadcasting.

"Sheet" Looks Weak

The absence of sustainers is costing publishers money. Appropriations set aside to plug up and coming new tunes are rapidly vanishing. The "sheet" looked woefully weak after a few days of the ban had elapsed. Pluggers declared it was the "worst thing in history" and could see no humor in the situation.

Shaw Grabs Lennie Hayton

Lennie Hayton, the leader-arranger-pianist, received a wire from Artie Shaw to take over the arranging end of things for Artie. And Lennie didn't hesitate. He went to the coast but fast.

Arthur Jarrett, the singer and former husband of Eleanor Holm, is being set in front of a band by the Rockwell office.

Teddy Powell Suit Settled

Alec Fila, young trumpeter with Bob Chester, will join Glenn Miller in Chicago shortly if his plans work out. . . Carol Kay is Russ Morgan's new sparrow. She's an ex-Woody Hermanite. . . G. Miller's Bluebird engraving of the song *WPA* will never be issued (Modulate to Page 20)

Morgan Pays 10G for His Own Contract

New York—Russ Morgan, trombone playing maestro, paid $10,000 to Charles Green of Consolidated Radio Artists in order to obtain his own contract and change Morgan booking affiliations to the Wm. Morris office.

Morgan made the deal two weeks ago, got his CRA release and has been jobbing around waiting for Morris moguls to get him some fat location jobs and one-nighters.

A Message From Mr. Weber

Congratulations, *Down Beat*, on your sixth anniversary. May you continue for many times six more anniversaries to present the musicians' news as honestly and constructively as you have in the past.

(Signed) JOSEPH N. WEBER
Honorary President and Technical Advisor of the A.F.M.

NBC, CBS Hit By His Sudden Ban

(More Details on Page 8)

New York—James C. Petrillo swept into New York as newly elected head of the American Federation of Musicians late in June and promptly jerked all dance bands off all sustaining programs on NBC. Three days later he applied the same treatment to CBS, leaving the

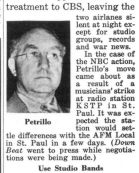

Petrillo

two airlanes silent at night except for studio groups, records and war news.

In the case of the NBC action, Petrillo's move came about as a result of a musicians' strike at radio station KSTP in St. Paul. It was expected the station would settle differences with the AFM Local in St. Paul in a few days. (*Down Beat* went to press while negotiations were being made.)

Use Studio Bands

Three nights later Petrillo, who only last month succeeded Joe N. Weber as AFM president, took similar action against CBS when an impasse was reached at station WRVA in Richmond, Va. CBS officials said Petrillo "attempted to order CBS to cease feeding sustaining dance remotes to WRVA. Columbia refused to quit the service, which is a CBS affiliate, and Petrillo then forbade all dance bands to play on remote control broadcasts for CBS."

Bands in New York, including both Dorseys, Charlie Barnet, Gray Gordon and many others, as well as bands in Chicago, Los Angeles and San Francisco, all suffered loss of air time by the edict. Most stations played records, or read news bulletins, or used small studio groups, to fill in the blank air time.

Songpluggers 'Go Crazy'

Mark Woods, NBC vice president, was dickering with Petrillo July 3 to settle differences. CBS leaders, at the same time, were trying to iron out their problem.

Many leaders and musicians were "sore" about their loss of broadcasting privileges. Others agreed that it was a "smart way" to get the St. Paul and Richmond musicians back to work. Song- (Modulate to Page 20)

No Bookings For Ziggy; BG Rests

Los Angeles—Inability to land bookings for Benny Goodman's band, without Benny leading it, will cause scuttling of plans to have Ziggy Elman front the crew and tour the nation while Benny takes a 6-week vacation, intimates of Goodman said last week.

The band was to leave the Casino on Catalina Island July 14 with BG leaving for a camp in the Maine woods immediately. Benny's spirits are high, but the sciatica ailment, which has partly paralyzed his leg, keeps him bent double most of the time. The band will probably break up, temporarily, while Benny fights to regain his health. Toots Mondello and Red Ballard are said to be remaining here to work in studio crews. The others, including Helen Forrest, will go separate ways unless bookings under Ziggy's leadership can be found, and that doesn't appear probable.

Awaits Movie . . .

Ginny Sims, brunet songstress with Kay Kyser, who records for Vocalion on the side with a small band of her own out of the Kyser combo, is set and ready to start on the RKO movie *You'll Find Out* which starts this month. Songs will be by Johnny Mercer and Jimmy McHugh. Meanwhile, she and Kyser's boys are vacationing at nearby beaches. Ginny recently had her nose "done over" via plastic surgery.

The Dorsey Brothers, Jimmy and Tommy, towered over most of the Big Bands in the late Thirties, with Tommy Dorsey and Glenn Miller on trombones. The failure of the brothers to achieve harmony in their personal relations led to the formation of their separate bands and the employment by Tommy Dorsey of a frail-looking singer called Frank Sinatra. By now, singers were coming to the forefront, Bing Crosby already well established with a string of hits like *Temptation* since his days with Paul Whiteman. Dick Haymes found popularity in the crooner mould, while Al Bowlly, soon to die in London's Blitz, had long since achieved equal billing with accompanying bands on his records.

PERSONNELS OF 1938's LEADING BANDS

SAX SECTIONS

Bands	1st Sax	2nd Sax	3rd Sax	4th Sax
1—Count Basie	Earl Warren (ha)	Lester Young (h)	Ronald Washington	Hershal Evans (h t & c)
2—Bunny Berigan	Milton Schatz	George Auld (h)	Gus Bivona (c)	Clyde Rounds
3—Larry Clinton	Mike Doty	Tony Zimmers (h)	Leo White (c)	Hugo Winterhalter
4—Bob Crosby	Joey Kearns	Eddie Miller (h)	Fazola (c)	Gil Rodin
5—Jimmy Dorsey	Milt Yaner	Herbie Hamyer (h)	Leonard Whitney	Charles Frazier (h)
6—Tommy Dorsey	Hymie Schertzer	Babe Russin (h)	Johnny Mince (c)	Dean Kincaide (h)
7—Duke Ellington	Otto Hardwick	Barney Bigard (hc)	Johnny Hodges (ha)	Harry Carney (hb)
8—Benny Goodman	Milton Yaner	Bud Freeman (h)	Dave Matthews (ha)	Arthur Rollini (h)
9—Glen Gray	Art Ralston	Pat Davis (h)	C. Hutchenrider (c)	Kenny Sargent
10—Horace Heidt	Frank DeVol	Bob Riedel	Bill Tieber	
11—Hal Kemp	Henry Dankers	Saxey Dowell	Ben Williams	Bruce Milligan
12—Gene Krupa	Bob Snyder	Sam Donahue (h)	Mascagni Ruffo	Sam Musiker (h)
13—Kay Kyser	Armand Buissaret	Morton Gregory	Herman Gunkler	Sully Mason
14—Guy Lombardo	Carmen Lombardo	Fred Higman	Lawrence Owen	Victor Lombardo
15—Jimmie Lunceford	Willy Smith (ha & c)	Joe Thomas (h)	Ted Buckner (ha)	Earl Carruthers
16—Glenn Miller	Hal McIntyre (c)	Gordon Beneke (h)	Wilbur Schwartz (c)	Stan Aaronson
17—Red Norvo	Frank Simeone	George Berg (h)	Hank D'Amico (c)	Maurice Kogan (h)
18—Artie Shaw	Les Robinson	Tony Pastor (h)	Hank Freeman	Ronny Perry
19—Chick Webb	Chauncey Haughton (c)	Ted McCrea (h)	Hylton Jefferson	Waymond Carver
20—Paul Whiteman	Al Gallodoro	Art Dollinger (h)	Sal Franzella (c)	Frank Gallodoro

BRASS SECTIONS

	1st Trumpet	2nd Trumpet	3rd Trumpet	1st Trombone	2nd Trombone
1—	Ed Lewis	Buck Clayton (h)	Harry Edison (h)	Dan Minor	Benny Morton (h)
2—	John Napton	Harry Goodman	Berigan (1st & h)	Nat LeBrousky	Ray Conniff
3—	Dappar Lloyd	Jimmy Fenton	Walter Smith (h)	Joe Ortolano	Ford Leary (h)
4—	Zeke Zarchi	Sterling Bose (h)	Bill Butterfield (1st & h)	Ward Silloway	Warren Smith (h)
5—	Ralph Muzzillo	Shorty Sherock (h)	Don Mattison (3 trmb)	Moe Zudecoff	Sonny Lee (h)
6—	Charlie Spivak	Vank Lausan (h)	Les Castalde (h)	Moe Zudecoff	Lou Jenkins (h)
7—	Wallace Jones	Cootie Williams (h)	Rex Stewart (h)	Lawrence Brown (h)	Juan Tizol (h)
8—	Harry James (h)	Ziggy Elman (h)	Chris Griffen (h)	Vernon Brown (h)	Red Ballard
9—	Frank Zullo	Grady Watts (h)	Sonny Dunham (h)	Billy Rausch	Peewee Hunt (h)
10—	Warren Lewis	Frank Strasek		Jimmy Skyles	
11—	Clayton Cash	Mickey Bloom (h)	Harry Wiliford (h)	Ed Kusborski (h)	Leo Moran
12—	Nick Prospero	C. Frankhauser (h)	Tom Goslin (h)	Toby Tyler	Bruce Squires (h)
13—	Robert Guy	Merwyn Bogue	H. Carriere	Harry Thomas	Max Williams
14—	Lebert Lombardo	Dudley Fodsick (mellophone)		Jim Dillon	
15—	Eddie Tompkins (h)	Paul Webster (h)	Sy Oliver (h)	James Young (h)	Russell Boles
16—	Bob Price	Bob Barker	Johnny Austin (h)	Al Mastren	Lightnin
17—	Johnny Owens	Jack Palmer (h)	Barney Zudecoff	Danny Russo	Al George
18—	John Best (h)	Claude Bowen	Chuck Peterson (h)	Russell Brown	George Arus (h)
19—	Dick Vance	Bobby Stark (h)	Taft Jordan (h)	Nat Storee	Sandy Williams (h)
20—	Don Moore	Charley Teagarden (h)	Harry Goldfield	Jose Gotierrez	Jack Teagarden (h)

RHYTHM SECTIONS AND VOCALISTS

	Piano	Guitar	Bass	Drums	Vocalists
1—	Count Basie	Freddy Green	Walter Page	Jo Jones	Helen Humes and James Rushing
2—	Joe Bushkin	Dick Morgan	Hank Wayland	Buddy Rich	Jayne Dover and Morgan
3—	Sam Mineo	Jack Chesleigh	Walter Hardman	Charlie Blake	Bea Wain & Chesleigh
4—	Bob Zurke	Nappy Lamare	Bob Haggart	Ray Bauduc	Marion Mann, Crosby, Lamare & Miller
5—	Freddy Slack	Roe Hilman	Jack Ryan	Ray McKinley	Bob Eberle & Mattison
6—	Howard Smith	Carmen Mastren	Gene Traxler	Maurice Purtill	Edythe Wright and Jack Leonard
7—	Duke Ellington	Fred Guy	Bill Taylor	Sonny Greer	Ivy Anderson
8—	Jess Stacey	Ben Heller	Harry Goodman	Dave Tough	Martha Tilton
9—	Howard Hall	Jacques Blanchette	Stan Dennis	Tony Briglia	Sargent and Hunt
10—	Lou Bush	Alvino Rey	Edward McKimey	Bernie Matthewson	Lysbeth Hughes, Larry Cotton, etc.
11—	Van Nordstrand		Jack Shirra	Emery Kenyon	Judy Starr, Bob Allen, Dowell & Wiliford
12—	Milton Raskin	Ray Biondi	Horace Rollins	Gene Krupa	Irene Daye & Leo Watson
13—	Lyman Gandee		Lloyd Snow	Eddie Shea	Ginny Sims, Harry Babbitt, Mason & Bogue
14—	Frank Vigneau	Francis Henry	Bernie Henry	George Gowans	Carmen & Lebert Lombardo
15—	Edwin Wilcox	Albert Norris	Mose Allen	Jimmy Crawford	Grissom, Oliver, Webster, Thomas & Young
16—	Chummy MacGregor		Rolly Bundoo	Bob Spangler	Marion Hutton, Ray Eberle, Beneke & Miller
17—	Bill Miller	Allen Hanlon	Pete Peterson	George Wettling	Mildred Bailey & Terry Allen
18—	Les Burness	Al Avola	Sid Weiss	Cliff Leeman	Billie Holiday
19—	Tommy Fulford	Bobby Johnson	Beverly Peer	Chick Webb	Ella Fitzgerald
20—	Roy Bargy	Art Ryerson	Artie Miller	Rollo Layland	Joan Edwards & Teagarden

OTHER MEN IN ABOVE BANDS 1. Dick Wells, 3rd & hot trmb. 5. Jimmy Dorsey, hot alto & cl. 6. Fred Stulce, 5th sax. Dorsey, hot & lead trmb; Elmer Smithers, 3rd trmb. 7. Joe Nanton, 3rd (plunger) trmb. 8. Goodman, hot cl.; Matthews also 1st sax. 9. Dan D'Andrea, 1st & 5th sax; Gray, 6th sax; Murray MacEachern, 1st & hot trmb. 12. Dalton Rizzotto' 3rd trmb. 15. Lunceford, Dan Grissom, saxes; Elmer Crumbley, 3rd & most hot trmb. 16. Bill Stagmire, 5th & hot trmb. Miller all hot & sweet trmb. 18. Shaw, hot cl.; Harry Rodgers, 3rd trmb. 19. Jefferson also 1st sax; George Matthews, 3rd trmb. 20. Bob Cusumano also 1st trpt; Hal Matthews, 3rd trmb.; Frank Signorelli, 2nd piano.

SYMBOLS: a, alto; b, baritone; c & cl, clarinet; h, hot; t, tenor; trpt, trumpet; trmb, trombone

from Metronome

By 1940, sales of records were again topping the hundred million mark and, though the roar of guns was the dominant sound in Europe, in America the beat of swing was calling the tune of a reviving economy.

In England, the Band Era followed a different path. While American bands were often doing the same thing with different levels of competence, British bands tended to be more versatile. Unlike America, where literally thousands of radio stations existed by the Forties, the British public had to make do with one, the BBC.

To broadcast on the radio was the ambition of every band because it was the only way to gain national popularity. Fees were low and the BBC's ambiguous attitude to bands – no doubt influenced by the austere director, John Reith – did not promote good relations (in 1935 the term 'hot music' was banned). Nevertheless, the BBC catered to popular taste with regular evening broadcasts – Lew Stone on Tuesdays, Harry Roy on Fridays, Ambrose on Saturdays. Such broadcasts, lasting ninety minutes, called for a varied repertoire and the bands could not restrict themselves to playing only rumbas or fox trots.

Though bands proliferated everywhere – my father led a band with the impressive title of The Wal-Norman Ambassadors – the big name bands played for the well-heeled clientele of the hotels, clubs and restaurants. This was in marked contrast to the States where the accessibility of big bands at concerts laid the foundations of the youth-orientated popular market.

AMBROSE BROADCAST WOW

MAY FAIR CELEBRITY GOES TO SAVOY HILL AND SHOWS THEM HOW

Special Report by
"DETECTOR" (JAN. 23 d)

LAST night, the B.B.C. did the right thing at last by presenting Ambrose and his Orchestra from the Savoy Hill Studios. It is hoped that other bands will be featured in the same way. The broadcast took place between eight and nine p.m.—the right time for dance music, because the majority of listeners prefer it so long as they don't have to stay up late to indulge their fancy.

The broadcast was a complete failure from one point of view, and that was that there was far too little publicity about it. It is time Ambrose had a live press agent in his organisation. Although he is entitled to far more publicity than what is given to many infinitely less able bands, he is well nigh starved.

The broadcast was, presumably, paid for by the B.B.C., but Ambrose provided such a largely augmented orchestra and such a wealth of special arrangements that it is evident he did the hour at a big personal loss.

In this respect Ambrose is out of court, as was Hylton when, three years ago, he accepted miserable terms for his famous studio broadcasts.

What's It Worth?

No artist should give the B.B.C. more service than it actually pays for. The B.B.C. can well afford to pay liberally for such tremendously attractive features, and next time they want the May Fair Orchestra they will have to pay for it adequately.

There is no doubt that Ambrose had taken the engagement with great seriousness, almost as if he were determined to show the country generally what he would do if he were running the B.B.C.'s own dance band.

He succeeded, and, if Jack Payne and Henry Hall listened in, they must have inwardly digested it all with great care.

There was little in the way of actual ballroom dance music played, the programme being on concert lines. Where big concert arrangements were employed, however, the band played with an expression which saved these orchestrations from sounding over-pretentious.

Naunton Wayne acted as compere and was a success, but could be more completely so. He is definitely an improvement on the usual dance band announcer.

The programme was, of course, mainly commercial, but it was well constructed.

Salient Points

For my own part, the points which pleased me most were the neatness of the rhythm section, the quality of the brass, the drumming of Max Bacon generally and particularly in "Tom Thumb's Drum," where, of course, he got more limelight, the vocals of Sam Brown all through—you've got to hand it to him—also the simple style singing of Elsie Carlisle, because what she does she does well, the wonderful playing of the O.K. Rhythm Kings' recording arrangement of "San Sue Strut" when Ambrose's *real* band only was employed, and Bert Read's piano solo of "Star Dust," which retained interest to the last bar.

I'm not cavilling at anything else in the programme, however, and if I have one criticism on the musical aspect it is that the sax section sounded a little thin, which does not disparage any member of it.

More studio-Ambrose, more publicity, and bigger fees are the salient lessons of this hopeful innovation.

Bert Ambrose

from Melody Maker

Although British bands toured the theatre circuits and drew mass popularity from radio and records, they were more often to be found in the clubs from where they broadcast, the hotels which could afford to maintain them. Roy Fox's band, which included Nat Gonella before he founded his Georgians, could be heard at the Monseigneur Restaurant; Lew Stone, whose line-up for a while included Al Bowlly and Nat Gonella, got you dancing at the Kit Kat – so did Joe Loss. The skilled musician Carroll Gibbons led the Orpheans at the Savoy. Ambrose, at the Embassy, the Mayfair and Ciro's, undoubtedly preferred the top hat to the cloth cap.

Despite the plush surroundings, the bands needed popular appeal and took every opportunity to plug their tunes on radio, not only to push record sales but to supplement their income with plug-money from the music publishers. A song plugged the night before could sell 5000 music sheets the day after. Even the afternoon broadcasts, which generally featured novelty songs for children, could result in a huge hit like Henry Hall's *Teddy Bears' Picnic*.

HYLTON PRESENTS CONTINENTAL BAND

Ray Ventura's Collegians at Palladium

Cementing the Musical Entente Cordiale

ONE of Jack Hylton's most interesting and spectacular undertakings came to fruition on January 18th, when the London Palladium's programme for the week was headed by Ray Ventura and his Collegians, the collection of ultra-keen French students who have made an enormous reputation on the Continent.

There is quite a romantic story behind the visit. Jack Hylton has been acquainted with Ray Ventura and his boys for a long time, and Ray has been one of the most ardent admirers of Jack's show. One particular night Jack Hylton had an opportunity of witnessing Ventura's show, and so impressed was he that he decided at once that London must see it.

When Jack sets his mind on a thing it is invariably accomplished, and, a specially good opportunity being provided by the fact that the Palladium management were minus a star act for that week, everything was fixed up at short notice and the band brought over.

That the venture was in every way justified was apparent from the very enthusiastic reception which the outfit received right from the first performance.

Jack Hylton himself was unable to be present at any time owing to his engagement at Leeds, but he sent a splendid telegram of encouragement which Ventura read out on the first night amidst enthusiastic applause.

Ventura and his sixteen followers put up a convincing show, with generally good musicianship. The show was entirely unconventional in many ways, and certainly provided something of which London had never before seen the like. The setting of the band, with the brass behind and the saxophone and string sections in front, was as unconventional as the white suits and particularly "easy" attitude of the boys.

The band played stylishly, but with plenty of restraint, using arrangements which seemed admirable for their purpose. Early in the programme a great rendering of "St. James' Infirmary," showed the boys' ability with this type of blues lament, and illustrated particularly the dramatic powers of the vocalist.

The extraneous stage-craft practised by Ventura was of a type quite new to London, and contained many excellent ideas, even if some of it seemed a little amateurish.

The peculiar combination of weakness and strength which characterises some of Ventura's efforts is particularly apparent in a sort of "meet the boys" number at the end of the programme. The first sax comes to the front and plays part of the "Merry Widow"— apparently for no particular reason, for there is nothing in his effort which could not be emulated by any ordinary saxophonist. Immediately afterwards the trombonist, tackling the difficult "Dancing Tambourine," gives an exhibition of skill and glorious tone which makes one feel that he has made a really fine contribution to the programme. After this one of the violinists does some comedy antics which are quite brilliant.

Ray Ventura's rise to fame has been a dramatic one. The son of a big French business man, he learned the piano and commenced a band at college. A trip to America was arranged, the boys playing on the boat, but when they got to New York their fame had arrived before them, and for a week they played all over the great capital, broadcasting from the Columbia studios.

On Ray's return to France the inevitable year's army service awaited him, and the band had to be dropped. Later he commenced again, promising his parents that if things did not go well he would throw up the game.

Things, as will be seen, have gone extremely well, and Ray, who is still only twenty-three, has returned home to play again at the Empire, Paris, and the Alhambra, Paris, whilst a trip to Canada is in prospect for next winter.

from Melody Maker

Though Ambrose's popularity could demand sixty record issues from him in one year, the premier European Show Band was Jack Hylton's (which had a good trumpet soloist in Jack Jackson). Rivalled only by Jack Payne, Hylton's band relied little on radio for its popularity, regularly playing to packed houses throughout Europe. Jack Hylton later found a new slot for himself as an impressario and was one of the few band leaders who fitted comfortably into television without his band.

Then came the War and with it came the invasion of Britain. Not, fortunately, an invasion by a goose-stepping army but by a bespectacled American major, Glenn Miller.

Though America had dominated popular song in the UK since the arrival of jazz over 75% of hits in 1930 came from America – Britain had kept her end up to a small extent in song-writing and to a large extent in performers. The Americans had a high volume of record sales in Britain but our home-grown products evened up the balance, even if only by imitation. Of course, the movies and the shows brought their hits across the Atlantic, highlighting how pathetic the British movies were, and the American bands had dedicated enthusiasts in Britain, but Jack Hylton was selling over three million records in 1930 and Jack Payne, at one stage, produced over ninety recordings in one year.

The War changed that by bringing live American bands to Britain. Since the early Thirties, such live music had not been heard in Britain because of differences between the British and American unions, so the impact of the Glenn Miller Band was more striking than Paul Whiteman's appearances in the Twenties.

from Downbeat

Roy Fox Set To Lead a Schmalz Crew

New York—Roy Fox, California-born maestro who gained fame in England as the "whispering cornetist," is back in rehearsal with a 13-piece band which will start out under GAC guidance shortly.

Fox, once musical director at the old Fox Film studios and later with Abe Lyman's band on trumpet, was in England from 1929, playing at the famous Café de Paris, Café Anglais and Kit-Cat with what was for years considered one of the country's three top bands. Ill health forced him to give up cornet. Last year he toured in Australia with a local band, returning to this country via California. The new group includes four saxes (doubling on strings and woodwind), one violin, three rhythm, and vocalist Kay Kimber. Myer Alexander is arranging. It'll be strictly a society band and a high-class location is in the offing.

Miller had achieved fame in the States after the appearance of his band in 1939 at the Glenn Island Casino led to a broadcasting contract. From then on, his live appearances created a tangible rapport with his audiences, his smooth-flowing sentimental sound – a mixture of swing, jazz and romantic ballads – becoming the unique style which was to be imitated by bands created after he was dead. In 1943 he organised the American Armed Forces Orchestra and in '44 he brought it to Britain. Miller was more than his music which, to some, may not have appeal. He was of his time, he fitted a hero's mould, the modest and musical soldier mysteriously disappearing into time. Without the uniform, without the death, the sound may not have been enough to keep the memory so alive.

from Downbeat

Squirmin' at the Sherman might be the title of this shot, by Ray Rising, which shows baritone Dick Todd switching places with Glenn Miller at Chicago's Hotel Sherman while Marion Hutton expostulates. Both Todd and the Miller menage record for Bluebird. Over at right Red Ingle, with fiddle, accompanies Elmo Tanner's whistling act with Ted Weems' band.

Swing had arrived late in Britain and hardly arrived at all in Europe. Essentially American, it reflected a country that was kicking off its Depression; it didn't fit in with a Europe that was plunging into a pit. While American youth was beginning to find dollars in its pockets and bobby-soxers were starting to scream for Sinatra to sing Sammy Cahn's *I'll Walk Alone*, European youth had no such bright horizon.

Sydney Moseley

GIVE IT A MISS

We Don't Want "Hot" Music
says
SYDNEY MOSELEY

The outbreak of war did not, as was first thought, put an end to live entertainment. Theatres and hotels stayed open, and bands, because of the difficulty of keeping musicians who were being called up, stayed put wherever they could be employed. Entertainment, in fact, boomed and Joe Loss, who managed to make the occasional tour – and still does – achieved sell-outs wherever he went.

The forces produced their own bands, the most popular being the Squadronaires who topped the Melody Maker poll of 1944 with Geraldo and Carl Barriteau. Many of the Squadronaires line-up came from Ambrose's band, whose singer, Vera Lynn, was the voice of British sentiment. Geraldo became supervisor of ENSA's Band Division and Ted Heath formed his band, inspired by Glenn Miller's, to give broadcasts on the BBC. V-Discs, produced by the Special Services Division of the American War Department, were played on American radio stations in Europe, to bring comfort to American troops and, coincidentally, complete the invasion of Europe by American popular music.

'British Jazz in Sad State'

New York—British jazz is in "a horrible state of affairs," says Leonard Feather, the isle's foremost champion of the cause.

Here making the rounds of niteries and bistros, and at the same time supervising a batch of special jam records for Decca, Feather admits there isn't much doing in

LEONARD FEATHER
the way of good music back home.

Crisis Hits Musicians In London

Ambrose's Future Uncertain . . . BBC's American Jam Session . . . Decca Lines Up All-Star British Swing Disc Series

By LEONARD G. FEATHER

LONDON.—Since the last London column was written for these pages, England has been through a spell of the jitters induced by war scare which hit nobody harder than the show folks. Entertainment reports all over were dead. A general atmosphere of pessimism prevailed, and even those who didn't have radios to keep them at home listening to propaganda speeches were not feeling in the mood to go out anyway.

Openings Dented

Jack Payne's new stage act was launched at the height of the crisis, and although the Prime Minister's speech that night was picked up in the theatre itself, the house was too sparse to give much encouragement to the band's show. Ambrose was similarly hit opening at the Holborn Empire in London.

After the situation had eased a bit things began to creep slowly back to normal, though for the first weeks of October there was still a noticeable slump in most attendances.

from Metronome

The end of the war saw the beginning of the end for the big bands. There was no immediate decline in terms of enthusiasm, but there were sudden disappearances and change. Many jazz players went back to jazz roots, New Orleans and blues. Boogie-woogie was born from a combination of the two, neatly epitomised in *Honky Tonk Train Blues* of Jimmy Yancey. Club owners, reeling under entertainment tax and rapidly rising prices, could not afford the big ensembles and 1946 saw the break up, in one month, of the bands of Benny Carter, Woody Herman, Harry James and Tommy Dorsey – though some later re-formed.

The war coincided with the development of be-bop, a move away from the sweet white music to the wilder black music, eventually to erupt in rock and roll. Side-men, bored with the routine of swing, went for the faster, freer tempos of Dizzy Gillespie, Lionel Hampton and Billy Eckstine. Jazz became a field for purists to dispute over hot or cool versions, bands split into smaller units, and television and teenagers put an end to the Brass Band Era. Many lingered on, with Count Basie and Duke Ellington ever

This Isn't Bunk; Bunk Taught Louis

By PARK BRECK

So many articles have been written by phonies who claim they started jazz that I hesitate to reveal the truth.

Through an investigation which has been made with great care and thoroughness by eight "critics" and record collectors during the last six months, startling facts have been uncovered. The facts have been checked and rechecked and are as close to the truth as will ever be known.

The writer can only disclose the most important at this time.

Letter Tells All!

In a letter to William Russell, owner of the world's most complete record collection, Willie "Bunk" Johnson, the cornetist who taught Louis Armstrong his first music, tells the story:

"Now here is the list about that jazz playing: King Buddy Bolden was the first man that began playing jazz in the city of New Orleans, and his band had the whole of New Orleans real crazy and running wild behind it. Now that was all you could hear in New Orleans, that King Bolden's Band, and I was with him. That was between 1895 and 1896, and we did not have any "Dixieland Jazz band" in those days. Now here is the thing that made King Bolden's band the first band to play jazz. It was because they could not read at all. I could fake like 500 myself, so you tell them that Bunk and King Bolden's band were the first ones that started jazz in that city or any place else. And now you are able to go ahead with your book."

Bunk Taught Louis!

Bunk has been acclaimed by many of the old time jazz musicians as the greatest cornetist of his day. There were three great cornetists, they say—Buddy, Bunk, and Louis. Their music was passed from one to the other. Bolden played a real "stomp trumpet," and Bunk added fast fingering, runs and high notes with a sweet tone. Then Louis combined the two styles with his own ideas to become the man who is recognized today as the greatest hot musician of all time.

The influence of King Oliver upon Louis has been exaggerated, but through no fault of those who claim that Oliver taught him. New facts now show that Louis had been playing for more than five

He Taught Louis ...Bunk Johnson, pictured with a shiny borrowed horn, taught Louis Armstrong more about blowing a trumpet than any other person, says Park Breck, whose true story of Louis' formative days is printed herewith. Bunk has no money now; he is badly in need of physical attention and many jazz lovers of New York are taking up a collection to help Bunk get a new start.

years before he joined Oliver's band.

Satchmo Agrees It's True

Sidney Bechet, Luis Russell, Pops Foster, Clarence Williams, Lil Armstrong and Louis himself all recognize Bunk as the greatest pioneer in hot jazz in the early part of the century.

Said Louis: "Bunk, he's the man they ought to talk about. What a man! Just to hear him talk sends me. I used to hear him in Frankie Dusen's Eagle band in 1911. Did that band swing! How I used to follow him around. He could play funeral marches that made me cry."

I'll let Bunk tell you in his own words of his influence on Louis—facts which Louis himself has corroborated:

"When I would be playing with brass bands in the uptown section (of new Orleans), Louis would steal off from home and follow me. During that time Louis started after me to show him how to blow my cornet. When the band would not be playing, I would let him carry it to please him. How he wanted me to teach him how to play the blues and *Ball the Jack* and *Animal Ball, Circus Day, Take It Away* and *Salty Dog* and *Didn't He Ramble?*, and out of all those pieces he liked the blues the best.

Blues Came First

"I took a job playing in a tonk for Dago Tony on Perdido and Franklin street and Louis used to slip in there and get on the music stand behind the piano. He would fool around with my cornet every chance he got. I showed him just how to hold it and place it to his mouth, and he did so, and it wasn't long before he began getting a good tone out of my horn. Then I began showing him just how to start the blues, and little by little he began to understand.

"Now here is the year Louis started. It was in the latter part of 1911 as close as I can think. Louis was about 11 years old. Now I've said a lot about my boy Louis and just how he started playing cornet. He started playing it by head."

Old-time musicians say that Louis' early records with King Oliver, Fletcher Henderson and blues singers were almost repetitions of the many licks he learned from Bunk. Bunk himself never recorded, and now I come to the sad part of his story:

Bunk played his cornet in bands throughout the deep South until 1933. Then the merciless tragedy which every musician dreads struck him—a physical handicap, put an end to that glorious music which was his life and soul.

I am sorry that Louis doesn't play those old blues any more, and I'm sorry that King Bolden is stomping trumpet in the Angel Gabriel's band. But my heart goes out to the artist who sold his trumpet and went to work in the fields at $1.75 a day to keep his body clothed and his soul on this earth.

"We have work only when rice harvest is in, and, that over, things go real dead until cane harvest," Bunk wrote in a letter. "I drive a truck and trailer and that pays me $1.75 a day, and that does not last very long. I'm down and in real deep need.

"I made up my mind to work hard until I die as I have no one to tell my troubles to, and my children cannot help me out in this case. I've been trying to get me $150 for three years, and I cannot make that kind of money here. Now I haven't got any other way but to put my shoulder to the wheel and my nose to the grinding stone and put my music down for good, and work. I cannot blow any more."

But with the help of modern dentistry Bunk can play again. Many persons who have heard of his plight have volunteered to subscribe to a fund to get him back on his feet.

"I want to become able to play trumpet once more. I know I can really play stomp trumpet yet," he says.

Louis Armstrong is giving his old teacher a trumpet, and promises of jobs for Bunk have come from many sources. Perhaps soon we will all have the opportunity to hear the man to whom we owe an unpayable debt of gratitude—the man who taught Louis Armstrong and thereby indirectly influenced the whole scope of modern swing music—Bunk Johnson.

---

popular in the States, and Billy Cotton, Ted Heath and Geraldo doing their British Thing in the UK, but their role was played increasingly in the background, and the commercial, formula-sounding bands were uneasy riders with the disc jockeys and the juke boxes. Their sound may yet revive but, at present, their popularity exists mainly through nostalgia.

The bands, though their popularity and influence was immense, were by no means the sole arbitrators of taste in what I have called the Lean Years. From the beginnings of the Depression through to the revival of fortunes in the late Forties, the hit songs continued to come from shows, movies, Tin Pan Alley – and from more remote areas.

Hill-billy songs found an ever-growing audience as juke boxes and radio stations penetrated rural communities, in the plains and in the mountains. The record companies, like Decca, soon sought out grass-root talent for hill-billy, blues and gospel recordings. The Singing Brakeman, Jimmie Rodgers, made and lost a fortune (as did his successor Hank Williams), his *I'm In The Jailhouse Now* being the voice of experience. Though not able to keep his money or his health, his songs spoke of sincere sentiment, his romanticisms came from the heart. His famous yodel was a curious Swiss–negro formula which, together with the nasal intonation, makes his records sound more like period pieces than enjoyable songs in their own right.

As hill-billy became country and western, the singing cowboys took over, Tex Ritter, Gene Autrey and Roy Rogers among them, establishing a whole genre of Western hits – *The Last Round Up*, *Empty Saddles* and *High Noon* leading the posse. After the war came the rise of Nashville, stimulated by the ASCAP dispute which sent the record companies in search of non-copyright material. Roy Acuff was perhaps a fair way away from Grand Ole Opry but his Nashville recordings preserved its traditions through to the Seventies.

The Lean Years were well nourished by the established pens of Gershwin, Rodgers and Hart, Hammerstein, Romberg, Dietz and Schwartz, Kern, Berlin and Porter. Perhaps the greatest of them all – and that's a dangerous statement to make – George Gershwin, died of a brain tumour in 1937, leaving *Porgy And Bess* as the greatest piece of American stage music yet written. Berlin, by the Forties the world's most popular songwriter, maintained a consistency of appeal with both temporary and permanent hits, heard in *Easter Parade* and *As Thousands Cheer*. From 1935 to '39 he abandoned the stage for Hollywood, turning in *Top Hat* and *Follow The Fleet*, and launched himself into the next decade and the war by appearing in his own show *This Is The Army* – which ran for four years. Not that those four years produced no other hits; in 1942 a song *White Christmas* was reasonably popular and may be heard today. *Always* was revived while *Annie Get Your Gun* was a box-office success in 1946 in the USA and in '47 in the UK (produced by Henry Hall in London with Lew Stone leading the orchestra).

Fred Astaire, whose legs inspired thousands of dancing schools to open in America and Britain much to the annoyance of many a child, appeared in Cole Porter's *Gay Divorce* in 1932 on Broadway before heading for Hollywood. Now showing his ability to be romantic as well as satirical, Porter was at his peak in 1934 with *Begin The Beguine*, *Night And Day* and *I've Got You Under My Skin*.

Rodgers and Hart were to veer from the romantic *Blue Moon* to the tougher lyrics of *Pal Joey*, Broadway's first anti-hero. This was a new style of musical, giving the Americans a closer look at the seamier side of life which Hart knew well. Rodgers had already been freed from his erratic partner before the latter's death in 1943 and Oscar Hammerstein II was the successful partner who teamed up for *Oklahoma*.

With one hit after another, *Oklahoma* was a show which did not need stars to make it successful. The running lyrics, mature characterisation, acting skills tied to good singing and hark-back to the secure days before the war, made up the successful formula for the promotion of the music, and *Oklahoma* guided musical theatre for the next twenty years.

While everybody couldn't get to the Broadway shows, most people could get to the cinema to hear Al Dubin and Harry Warren's hit *We're In The Money* while watching the Gold Diggers of 1933. The Gold Diggers always struck lucky, both in and out of the films, giving Dubin and Warren one of many hits in thirty-five with *Lullaby Of Broadway* and following this with *Forty-Second Street*. Hollywood owes much to this pair and particularly to Harry Warren who wrote over two hundred songs for fifty movies.

Films did not have to be musicals to launch hit songs; they could be plays with songs written into them, vaguely referring to the plot, or they could simply be the theme song from the film – many of which were straightforward adaptations from classical music. Bing Crosby sang the Screen Song of the Year 1937, *Sweet Leilani* – which won Harry Owens an Oscar – in the film *Waikiki Wedding*. The same year another film score sold more copies than any other individual song in 1937; it was the score of Disney's *Snow White* which included *Whistle While You Work* and *Heigh Ho*. Four years before, another Disney song had been a hit all over the world. Sung, apparently, by three little pigs, *Who's Afraid Of The Big Bad Wolf* was analysed for social comment and political portent not, I suspect, with much foundation.

While Tin Pan Alley was vastly over-producing, pouring out a lot of unenduring rubbish and relatively few standards, the films were still turning out good songs. *September In The Rain* (Al Dubin and Harry Warren), *That Old Feeling* (Lew Brown and Harry Fain) and *Don't Fence Me In* (Cole Porter, sung by Bing Crosby and the Andrews Sisters) were the quality songs that were the rule rather than the exception. Singers like Judy Garland and Fred Astaire simply had the choice of the best material, and Hollywood could afford to pay the highest prices.

Though Tin Pan Alley was over-reaching itself, with poor material being plugged into brief hits, good songs found their way out of the morass to become the standards of today. For example, Bing Crosby collaborated with Roy Turk and Fred Ahlert on *Where The Blue Of The Night Meets The Gold Of The Day* which showed that the public wasn't entirely blinded by the popularity of Moises Simons' *The Peanut Vendor* (Simons did a little better with Arthur Tracy's signature tune *Marta*).

The Alley's problem was how to supply an insatiable demand and make enough money out of declining sheet music sales. If *Beer Barrel Polka* could sell half a million copies in six months, it was inevitable that songs with the quality of Jerome Kern's *Smoke Gets In Your Eyes* should give way to a more banal but easily recalled melody line for the sake of quick turnover.

Britain's Tin Pan Alley, in Denmark Street, suffered from the same problems although buying rights to American hits meant certainty of success for the British publisher. Americans had less interest in British songs but there were exceptions. Noel Coward had an American success with *Some Day I'll Find You* and *I'll Follow My Secret Heart*. Kennedy and Grosz's *Isle Of Capri* was followed by *Red Sails In The Sunset*, *Poor Little Angeline*, and *Harbour Lights* (a hit for Rudy Vallee in 1937) and Jimmy Kennedy teamed up with Michael Carr to produce the 1940 American No.1 *South Of The Border;* for No.2, Kennedy produced *My Prayer* with George Boulanger – a hit for the Inkspots. So the trans-Atlantic traffic was not all one-way.

The Second World War did not produce such endearing songs as the well-remembered choruses of the 1914–18 War. People on both sides of the Atlantic were more aware of what war involved and less inclined to beat the drum and blow the brass. There were patriotic songs – Berlin's *God Bless America* of 1917 was revived almost as a national hymn. *Lili Marlene* was the toast of all sides and the barrel was rolled out

Vera Lynn

heartily by the allies who preferred a down to earth tune to the more sentimental ballads. The latter were not lacking, particularly those of Vera Lynn which have come to rival the First World War songs. *Now Is The Hour*, of which Gracie Field's recording outsold Bing Crosby's, was a hit after the war but remains associated with the sentiment of the war years.

The British produced a crop of peculiarly British songs – *Kiss Me Goodnight, Sergeant Major* and *Nursey, Nursey* (Harry Leon and Don Pelosi), *Somewhere In France* (Michael Carr), *Run Rabbit Run* and *Let The People Sing* (Noel Gay) and *We're Going To Hang Out The Washing On The Siegfried Line* (Kennedy and Carr). Nice songs, not brilliant, but likeable and of their time. Some songs were more sharply directed, as *Berlin Or Bust, Even Hitler Had A Mother* and *A Very Little Nazi*, but they didn't survive the war. Perhaps they were too explicit. The slower, more sad songs were less rousing and more popular with the civilians, like the heart-pulling *Who's Taking You Home Tonight*. These songs were frowned upon by the BBC who felt that stirring, upper-lip songs were needed for the short-wave radios in the shelters.

America liked *The White Cliffs Of Dover* and *When The Lights Go On Again*, but the Army really preferred *Don't Sit Under The Apple Tree* which possibly echoed the troops' main worries about home. Irving Berlin did his bit with *This Is The Army Mister Jones* and the Air Force had *Coming In On A Wing And A Prayer*. *White Christmas*, too, could rightly be interpreted as a war song, a longing for home.

America had a peculiarly domestic problem in the music industry during the war, a squabble between ASCAP and the record companies. Live recording was banned (except for the V-discs) and many songs appeared with solely vocal backing. Old records were re-issued (Rudy Vallee's 1931 disc of *As Time Goes By* was a big hit in '43) and the formation of Broadcast Music Incorporated led to a rejuvenation of hill-billy and blues songs which ultimately paved the way for the popularity of rhythm and blues.

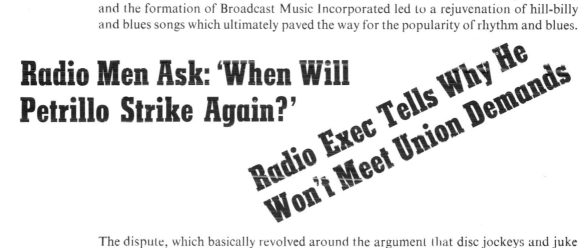

The dispute, which basically revolved around the argument that disc jockeys and juke boxes were doing away with live entertainment and hence musicians, was eventually resolved by the capitulation of the recording companies to the American Federation of Musicians. Though the dispute was to occur again – and the argument still goes on – its resolution gave composers a chance to re-establish themselves; the professionals like Johnny Mercer and Harold Arlen were back with *Blues In The Night* and *That Old Black Magic*.

How, in the midst of all the varied offerings of the music world during the Lean Years, did Francis, Day & Hunter cope? Partly through initiative which made them open Paris and Berlin offices (the latter a more dubious investment in the late Thirties when hints about Jewish composers became more pointed), partly through the by now established practice of buying American hits – sometimes whole catalogues – and publishing them in England. When the Depression was really biting in England, F, D & H were able to pay the rent for their offices with the proceeds from William Smallwood's perennial Piano Tutor, first published in the 1880s.

By 1930 the record companies were making the profits which the music publishers had once thought to be their own. The publishers soon negotiated a royalty, a minimum of three-farthings per side, which proved very necessary as sheet music further declined in sales. Pretty soon, however, record sales were in the doldrums as competition grew fierce, prices were cut with Woolworths selling nine-inch discs at six old pence each and popular artists demanded higher fees. Song-plugging was expensive, with money passing

MEN BEHIND THE HITS
No. 2—FRANCIS, DAY & HUNTER, LTD.

Jack Lorimer   Charlie Lucas   Eddie Day

INTRODUCING YOU TO THE PROFESSIONAL STAFFS OF THE MUSIC PUBLISHING FIRMS WHOSE WORK IT IS TO PUT OVER THE SONGS THAT YOU PLAY AND SING

EDDIE DAY, one of the Directors of the firm, is in charge of the Professional Department and has been guiding the popular music policy of F. D. and H. for some fifteen years. During this time, he has been concerned with some of the greatest numbers in song history, these including such smash-hits as Irving Berlin's *What'll I Do?; Because I Love You; You Forgot To Remember;* the famous *When You And I Were Seventeen;* and other sensations.

Each of these songs made a fortune, and Eddie Day is justly proud of the part he played in putting them over on this side of the water.

A much-travelled man, he has been to America, Australia, Paris, Berlin and elsewhere on the firm's business, and is at present guiding the fortunes of a number which is sweeping the country, this being *Goodbye Sally,* written by Arthur Riscoe and John Borelli. He is confident that this is going over very big, and he and his Department also have high hopes of the new dance, *The Black-Out Stroll,* and a new waltz, *Who's Taking You Home To-night?*

JACK LORIMER, son of the late Jock Lorimer, the famous Scots comedian, is about the only Professional Manager in the business who is also actively engaged in broadcasting and recording the songs he helps to put over. Did you hear him this week, singing with Jay Wilbur's Band, at the B.B.C. country headquarters?

Jack is one of the original members of the Rhythm Brothers, whose broadcasts with Ambrose were so popular, and he is also famous as an arranger for vocal trios, the Carlyle Cousins (to quote but one example) owing much of their success to his arrangements.

He joined the F. D. and H. firm about ten years ago, and has since risen to be Professional Manager, a job which he handles with the greatest capability.

* * *

CHARLIE LUCAS, younger brother of Sun's Bert Lucas, has been with F. D. and H. for over thirty years, which must be something of a Charing Cross Road record for long service. He joined the firm in 1909, as office-boy, lighting fires and washing floors as part of his duties. Now, he is one of the stalwarts of the Professional Department, having grown up with the profession, and possessing a tremendously wide knowledge of every branch of popular music.

Charlie took Melville Gideon's place as pianist of the Original Ragtime Octet, which came over here from America, and he became one of the earliest exponents of ragtime, playing such numbers as *Hitchy Koo, Waiting For The Robert E. Lee,* etc.

He was coached by the famous Leslie Stuart, composer of *Lily of Laguna,* and has since had the handling of this writer's work for F. D. and H., in addition, of course, to the hundreds of other songs which he helps to put over.

from Melody Maker

to artists, band leaders and radio producers for the necessary plug. And it wasn't always money; houses may be built, cars may be supplied, new suits could be delivered.

Song-plugging has more sinister overtones today than it did until the Fifties. Though the BBC tried many times to stamp it out, they eventually came to terms with plugging and established payment scales, though finally bringing payments to an end in 1947. The music publishers relied on their song-pluggers for publicity and the radio was the best way of advertising. Since British films were, on the whole, simply not comparable to American films, and since most of America's tunes could find a market in Britain without the reverse being true, the pluggers had to get those American songs into somebody's repertoire. To do that, he had to have a good ear, a glib tongue, a full wallet and a smooth elbow.

Britain's Tin Pan Alley was as much prone to poaching as America's. Song-pluggers waited in Denmark Street doorways to catch composers and arrangers, steering them into the offices and sitting them at pianos. Occasionally a composer could pull a fast one.

Harry Leon, who sold his rights to *Sally* for £30, teamed up with Leo Towers and the pair went under contract in 1932 to F, D & H, being paid £20 a week each. Being under contract, they could not offer a song to another publisher for more money without having a release note. Eddie Day, now running F, D & H, had no wish to lose their songs and no wish to publish them if he didn't like them.

Leon and Towers found a solution. They persuaded Charlie Lucas, the Professional Manager, to play their songs so badly to Eddie Day that he immediately gave Lucas a release note. This was then passed to the pair in The Royal George, the Alley pub, and Lucas was passed a note of thanks in return. A complicated way of selling a song.

During the war, F, D & H stayed put in Charing Cross Road, ducking the bombs. One unexploded bomb sat menacingly in front of the shop for a day before it decided to fulfill its purpose in life. It blew a hole in the basement, filling it with water and ruined stock. The basement was shored up, more stocks of scarce and badly-made paper were conjured up mysteriously and work continued for another two months before the second unexploded bomb was discovered and a rapid exit effected. This time the bomb was an incompetent failure.

The war ended, the lights went on again, swing faded and nobody knew what was coming next. The singers seemed here to stay; Bing, Sinatra, Dick Haymes, Perry Como, Frankie Laine, Eddie Fisher, Nat King Cole – there were plenty of singers, waiting for a new style.

In Britain we were queuing up and clearing up, and George Formby and Izzy Bonn went on forever. In the States, young kids were buying records, be-bopping in high school, even running cars. They were demanding kids and they were getting what they demanded.

They now demanded rock and roll.

Louis Armstrong

129

I'LL GET BY
(AS LONG AS I HAVE YOU)

Words by
ROY TURK

Music by
FRED E. AHLERT

F. & D. Ltd. 21308

131

BROADWAY MELODY.

Written by
ARTHUR FREED.

Composed by
NACIO HERB BROWN.

Moderato.

Don't bring a frown to old Broad-way, You've got to clown on Broad way.

legato.

You Were Meant For Me.

Words by
ARTHUR FREED.

Music by
NACIO HERB BROWN.

Moderato.

You were meant for me, I was meant for you.

Where is the Song of Songs for Me?

WALTZ SONG.

Words and Music by
IRVING BERLIN.

Valse moderato.

Where is the song of songs for me? Beau-ti-ful song of ec - sta - sy;

PAGAN LOVE-SONG.

Words by
ARTHUR FREED.

Music by
NACIO HERB BROWN.

Not too fast

Come with me where moon-beams Light Ta-hi-tian skies,

PRICE TWO SHILLINGS EACH.
FRANCIS, DAY & HUNTER, Ltd., 138-140, Charing Cross Road, London. W. C. 2.

SINGIN' IN THE RAIN.

Words by
ARTHUR FREED.

Tune Ukulele.
4 3 2 1
A D F# B

Music by
NACIO HERB BROWN.

Sing - in' in the rain,   Just sing - in' in the rain,   What a

F.&D.Ltd. 18719.

glo - ri - ous feel - ing, I'm hap - py a - gain! I'm

laugh - ing at clouds, So dark, up a - bove, The

sun's_ in my heart_ And I'm read - y for love. Let the

storm - y clouds chase Ev - 'ry - one_ from the place, Come

D. & D.Ltd.18719.

on＿ with the rain, I've a smile＿ on my face. I'll

walk down the lane With a hap-py re-frain, And

sing-in',＿ just sing-in' in＿ the rain.＿＿＿＿＿

1. Why am I smil-in' and why do I sing? Why does De did
2. Why do they call me the boy with the smile? When did I

-cem-ber seem sun-ny as Spring Why do I get up each
find out that Life is worth while? Why do I treat all my

morn-ing to start— Hap-py and het up, with joy in my heart?
trou-bles with scorn? See-ing the rain-bow be-fore it is born.

Why is each new task a tri-fle to do?— Be-
Why am I sure all my dreams will come true? Be-

D.S. al Fine

cause I am liv-ing a life full of you.—
cause I am bank-ing my whole world on you.— I'm

F. & D. Ltd . 18719.

137

Love Is The Sweetest Thing.

Additional Lyric by
Charles Wilmott.

Words and Music by
RAY NOBLE.

F.& D.Ltd.19419.

-ness to ev-'ry-thing As Love's old sto-ry. Love is _____ the strang-est thing, No song of

birds up-on the wing Shall in our hearts more sweet-ly sing Than Love's old sto-ry. What-ev-er

heart may de-sire, What-ev-er Fate may send, This is the tale that nev-er will tire,

This is the song with-out end. Love is _____ the great-est thing, The old-est

yet the la-test thing, I on-ly hope that Fate may bring Love's sto-ry to you. _____ you.

K01.03.33.   F. & D. Ltd.19419.

141

Who's Afraid Of The Big Bad Wolf?

From WALT DISNEY'S SILLY SYMPHONY
"THE THREE LITTLE PIGS."

Words and Music by
FRANK E. CHURCHILL
and ANN RONELL.

F.&D. Ltd. 19639.

built his house with hay; With a hey-hey toot, he blew on his flute, And he played a - round all
big bad wolf- ie's breath; "By the hair of your chin-ny-chin, I'll blow you in," And the twig house an-swered

day. Num-ber Two was fond of jigs, And so he built his house with twigs, Hey did-dle did-dle, he
"Yes." No one left but num-ber Three To save the pig-let fam-i-ly, When they knocked, he

played on his fid - dle and danced with la - dy pigs; Num - ber Three said, "Nix on tricks, I will
fast un-locked and said, "Come in with me!" Now they all were safe in - side; And the

build my house with bricks." He had no chance to sing and dance, 'Cause work and play don't
bricks hurt wolf-ie's pride. So he slid down the chim-ney, and oh, by Jim-ney, In the fi - re he was

mix! Ha - Ha Ha! The two lit-tle, do lit-tle pigs Just winked and laughed Ha-Ha!
fried! Ha - Ha Ha! The three lit-tle, free lit-tle pigs Re - joiced and laughed Ha-Ha!

F & D. Ltd . 19639.

BLUE MOON.

Words by
LORENZ HART.

Music by
RICHARD RODGERS.

The letters below Bass Stave indicate names of Chords for Piano Accordion & Guitar

Sub published by Robbins Music Corp. Ltd. London
Assigned 1975 to Big 3 Music Ltd. for Great Britain and the Commonwealth,
Mortimer House, 37/41 Mortimer St., London W.1

F. & D. Ltd.19888.

F. & D. Ltd 19888.

Rhythm Of The Rain.
(La Romance De La Pluie.)

Words by
JACK MESKILL.

Music by
JACK STERN.

Moderato.

I love the rhythm of the raindrops, To hear the pitter pattering rhythm of the raindrops While others skitter scatter, I

Singing A Happy Song.
(Le Chapeau D'paille.)

Words by
JACK MESKILL.

Music by
JACK STERN.

Moderato.

The sun's shin-ing, There's no pin-ing, Your hat's lined with a sil-ver lin-ing, And you're hap-py when

When I Grow Too Old To Dream.

Words by
OSCAR HAMMERSTEIN II.

Music by
SIGMUND ROMBERG.

Valse lento.

When I grow too old to dream, I'll have you to re-mem-ber.

The Night Is Young.

Words by
OSCAR HAMMERSTEIN II.

Music by
SIGMUND ROMBERG.

Andante affettuóso.

The night is young and the moon is rid-ing high.   The night is young

PRICE SIXPENCE EACH.

FRANCIS, DAY & HUNTER, Ltd., **138-140**, Charing Cross Road, London W.C. **2**.

A-Tisket A-Tasket

Words and Music by
ELLA FITZGERALD and AL FELDMAN

The letters below Bass Stave indicate names of Chords for Piano Accordion & Guitar

S.M.Co.Ltd. 1201

S.M.Co.Ltd.1201

Printed in London, England by The Compton Printing Works (London) Ltd.

151

A-Tisket A-Tasket

PIANO ACCORDION SOLO
Special simplified arrangement by
DUDLEY E. BAYFORD

All Counter Basses underlined A *etc*.

Words and Music by
ELLA FITZGERALD
and AL FELDMAN

Moderato (*steadily*)

S.M.Co. Ltd. 1201

Who's Taking You Home To-night?

Words by
TOMMIE CONNOR

Tune
Ukulele
Bb Eb G C

Music by
MANNING SHERWIN

1. They met at a dance, In a waltz of ro-mance Stran-gers, but strange as it seems, The girl's heart was thrilled A dream was ful-filled At these words from the boy of her dreams.

2. The bride wore a smile When she walked down the aisle. Filled with the joy of ro-mance. She'll nev-er for-get That night when they met And these words that she heard at the dance.

CHORUS

WHO'S TAK-ING YOU HOME TO-NIGHT Af-ter the dance is

The letters below Bass Stave indicate names of Chords for Piano Accordion & Guitar

F. & D. Ltd. 20752

F. & D. Ltd. 20752
Printed in London, England by The Compton Printing Works (London) Ltd.

Don't Sit Under The Apple Tree
(WITH ANYONE ELSE BUT ME)

© 1942 Robbins Music Corp. Ltd. USA
Sub published by Robbins Music Corp. Ltd. London
Assigned 1975 to Big 3 Music Ltd for Great Britain and the Commonwealth
Mortimer House, 37/41 Mortimer St., London W.1

S. M. Co. Ltd. 1358

Extra Couplets

Though Navy Blue may appeal to you when you meet a bold Jack Tar,
Don't be a sport when the Fleet's in port 'cos you know what sailors are. So!

Be dumb and deaf when the R.A.F. say "The moon is shining bright!"
They might take sips from your red lips as "The Target for to-night!" So!

That apple tree knows the history of our meetings after dark,
I'd hate to find other names entwined with yours, upon the bark. So!

You sat with me 'neath the apple tree when I stole our first love kiss,
I won't deny Ma's apple pie ain't the only thing I miss. So!

S.M.Co.Ltd.1358

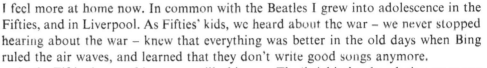

5
POPULAR AND POP

Bill Haley

I feel more at home now. In common with the Beatles I grew into adolescence in the Fifties, and in Liverpool. As Fifties' kids, we heard about the war – we never stopped hearing about the war – knew that everything was better in the old days when Bing ruled the air waves, and learned that they don't write good songs anymore.

As the Fifties began, things were still a bit grey. The 'brickies' or bomb sites were our playgrounds, sugar was on ration, we ate too much spam and there were too many veterans of both wars still looking for the promise of the new dawn. We collected American comics, saw American films, admired American cars and, like our parents before us, listened to American music. Our grandparents were at one end of the hundred years covered in this book, still uncomfortable with the sound of those 'effeminate' crooners, and we were at the other, ready for something new.

In America, the 'generation gap' was invented to account for the vagaries and virtues of the new concept of 'teenager'. The youth cult was laying its foundations, the squeals of the infants were being monitored so that their squeals of adolescence could be catered for. A new generation, untutored by deprivation, was growing which would not take no for an answer. These are, naturally, generalisations but they give the tone of the new era, the changes from which the cliché of the 'revolution of youth' was born.

Though the 'New Look' set the fashion in 1949, there was not much indication of the changes that were to take place in popular music. The bobbysoxers still screamed for Frank Sinatra though a lull in popularity put Billy Eckstine at the top of the polls with Sinatra way down on the list. The new face of Guy Mitchell became familiar as *My Heart Cries For You* made a hit out of a song rejected by Sinatra. Frankie Laine's *Jezebel* put him among the heart-throbs and Nashville's Hank Williams gave Tony Bennett an untypical country and western hit *Cold Cold Heart*.

The big bands, as we have seen, had gone into their decline. There were many still around: Stan Kenton, Duke Ellington, Benny Goodman and a re-formed Count Basie's Band kept their popularity and a revival of the Glen Miller sound, to be repeated in the Sixties and Seventies, kept them within the realm of popular music, but they would never be part of the new concept of 'pop'.

Nor would musicals, however successful, however popular. *South Pacific, Guys And Dolls, Annie Get Your Gun, The King And I*, all these theatre musicals and their subsequent films produced standards of enduring popularity, but their breeding stables were governed by the traditions established in the decades preceding the Fifties. *My Fair Lady* and *Gigi* kept those traditions alive in the Fifties but *West Side Story* demonstrated an awareness of an altered taste and by 1967 pop music had given *Hair* an altogether different style of musical theatre – though nonetheless valid and exciting.

What, then, made pop into a different category to popular music?

The lines are not distinct and the boundaries so often converge that it is impossible to distinguish between the two. But there are some factors that underline the differences.

Age is probably the dominant factor. As the Fifties progressed, pop music increasingly became the domain of the teen-and-twenties, the artists peaked their popularity in their twenties, and the beat grew faster to absorb the energies of youth. Though rock and roll was to be the catalyst of change, the growth of pop as a youth cult in the Fifties was a gradual process which accelerated in the early Sixties and burst

Frank Sinatra

159

into flames with the Beatles, the pop festivals and the supergroups.

Affluence went hand in hand with youth. Young people could afford to buy records, their own clothes, go to their own dances, form their own clubs. They therefore developed their own taste, prompted by a society which saw them as a distinct entity from their parents who increasingly lost confidence in their own life-style, persuaded that the 'generation gap' was a physical barrier which could not be crossed. Mary Quant took the hint and dressed the dolly birds of the Sixties, fashions only for the young – or those that could look young. No longer did children have to ape the dress of their elders; when Gilbert O'Sullivan first appeared in cloth cap and braces, he was regarded as an anachronism, a speciality act. In the Forties, the audience would have merely assumed that he was too poor to buy a suit.

Pop, too, centred around the singer rather than the song – the composer seemed rrelevant. Who wrote *Rock Around The Clock*? Later the sound, the good vibes, was to be more important than the song; indeed the word 'song' carries with it connotations of the Thirties rather than the Seventies. But in 1952 it was the singer that had them screaming, it was Johnny Ray that was written across their sweaters. *Cry* meant what it said and the thin worried-looking youth with the hearing aid sobbed all the way to the bank while his fans boo-hooed in the balconies. Advance sales of records before release were soon to reach the half-million mark for Elvis, the Beatles and the Stones – for a sound that was still to be heard!

Technical improvements in the production of discs gave an impetus to pop music. By the mid-Fifties, 45s and EPs had dislodged the heavy and breakable 78s, micro-groove long-playing records had been on the market since 1948 (Johnny Ray's first LP sold 250,000 copies in the USA) and hi-fi, automatic turntables, pick-ups, three speeds and built-in amplifiers became an essential part of the whole kit and caboodle of pop. In the Sixties, stereo and quadrophonic sound make equipment more comprehensive and in the Seventies the cassette began to push its way into the market. The sound of the record improved, recording techniques lifting the voice from the background and placing it intimately in the room. Mitch Miller of Columbia Records started adding echo to the singer's voice, making sure that a singer could rarely give a live version of his own hit. Some singers, like Del Shannon and John Leyton, were often more echo than voice.

Finally, the mass media, the exploiters of superlatives, created pop. Artists – lousy, mediocre or good – were 'hailed' as 'smash sensations', they 'lashed out' at their critics, they 'swept' to the top. Their publicity offices were good, stirring up fake frenzied riots – as for Bill Haley – to lead the way for real riots. In the Sixties, fan worship became religion as the Beatles and the Stones received – and accepted – worship from the millions. The Sixties completed the unity of pop, and marked its exclusiveness. Isle of Wight, Woodstock, Bath, all the pop festivals provided the places of worship; the clothes, the hair, the drugs, the slogans were the vestments and litanies; the groups were the high priests; and the gods? – were themselves. Youth, believing in nothing better, knowing nothing worse, finally worshipped itself.

But we have leapt ahead. Back in 1950 people of all ages were simply buying the songs they liked and, apart from Johnny Ray who inspired many a jaundiced eye, there were few shocks in this somewhat somnolent world. Perry Como cruised to the top of the newly-established charts with *If*, Vera Lynn topped the USA charts – the first English performer to do so – with *Auf Wiederseh'n* and Al Martino topped the first New Musical Express charts with *Here In My Heart*. Winifred Atwell literally sold millions of records before heading down under, Walt Disney's *Cinderella* comfortably reassured the children and Gene Autrey looked after Christmas deliveries with *Rudolph The Red Nosed Reindeer*. There were no strict classifications; Mario Lanza, Huddie Ledbetter and Johnny Ray could all have hits at the same time.

For Britain, it was a time of near-complete submission to the USA. If it was American, it sold and all the British could do was to issue cover records as soon as the disc was released. I can remember the irritation I felt looking at American Hit Charts which contained few, if any, British records, while American singers bestrode our charts with scarcely a disdainful glance at their imitators. Elvis, who could count on a certain No.1 hit in the UK with any release, never did come here. We remembered that in the Sixties when Merseysound knocked Nashville for six.

Elvis was one of the Fifties' biggest sensations; the other was rock and roll. They

Johnnie Ray

Winifred Atwell

Tommy Steele   *Adam Faith*

both had their roots in rhythm and blues and its derivative, country and western, and they both aroused the masses, particularly the young. It was a cliché of that time – and of our time, I suppose – that the young were bored, and it may have been true. At any rate, youth had money and leisure and they spent it avidly and eagerly on the new exciting rhythm of rock.

Rock and roll, a phrase coined by an American disc jockey Alan Freed from the lyrics of rhythm and blues, was the big departure from tradition. It gave us Teddyboys in their drapes, violence and excitement. It gave youth its own heroes – Elvis, of course, and Little Richard, Jerry Lee Lewis, Gene Vincent, Eddie Cochran, Tommy Steele, Buddy Holly, the Big Bopper and dozens of others, as acceptable to the kids as they were unacceptable to the parents. They preached nothing revolutionary; they merely spun the kids' heads. Bill Haley led them all, with the Comets and some contrived publicity. When *Rock Around The Clock* came to the UK, the newspapers were told that cinemas were wrecked in the USA as a result of the film. The stories were printed and immediately the Teds slashed through thousands of cinema seats. I remember a brand new cinema in Bootle being wrecked after the first showing of the film. I also remember a fourteen-year-old teenager, Frankie Lymon, being mobbed outside Liverpool's Empire where he sang, with the Teenagers, his dual hit *Baby Baby/ I'm Not A Juvenile Delinquent*.

The British, with only one radio station playing pop, a more restricted financial outlook and an inferiority complex resulting from a diet of cover records which never sounded as good as the real thing, went wholeheartedly for rock and took it to themselves. They not only produced the profoundly versatile Tommy Steele; they launched Cliff Richard, Terry Dene, Marty Wilde, Billy Fury, Eden Kane and a cast of thousands. None of these was a pure rocker, all of them being as likely to produce a nasally-sentimental ballad as a fast-beat swinger.

The British also produced skiffle. Home-made music, a broom handle nailed to a box, mixed with guitars and drums, and a lot of gusto. Lonnie Donegan was regarded as the King of Skiffle, but he was a mixture of rock, ballad, folk and the trad jazz of Chris Barber from whence he sprang. Skiffle, as rock took its hold, turned into folk music and eventually emerged in the Sixties, with its American counterpart, as folk pop.

By now there were established singers whose fame had been created by the record companies, whose records sold in millions, and who stood alone in their popularity, without a band or a group behind them. Elvis was King and his abandoning of rock and roll for ballads served only to increase the age span of his audience without

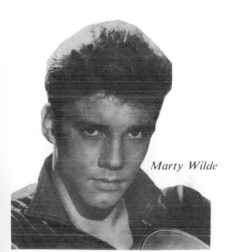

Marty Wilde

IT'S ONLY MAKE BELIEVE

Words & Music by CONWAY TWITTY and JACK NANCE

Featured by
CLIFF RICHARD

2/-

FRANCIS, DAY & HUNTER, LTD., 138-140, Charing Cross Road. London. W.C.2.

Cliff Richard

alienating his teenage fans. Pat Boone stood next only to Elvis with, in 1957, seventeen different records selling at the same time. While American singers, like Tennessee Ernie Ford, Ricky Nelson and Paul Anka were as well known in the UK as in the States, the reverse was seldom true; Laurie London, Dickie Valentine, Cliff Richard, even Tommy Steele had great difficulty in getting known in the USA.

Black singers, like black jazz players, were popular without there being a particular reference to colour. The singing groups, like the Platters, the Inkspots and the Drifters, tended to conform to the values of a white society, their race being only perceptible in their harmonies and their rhythm and blues–based beat. Mixed with the soul of the gospel singers, the resulting commercial sound of the Dominoes and the Orioles gave the base to Motown and the sound of Tamla Motown in the Sixties. It was a sad

The Drifters

Max Bygraves

the artists could not play or sing their own records (such a finger was pointed at the Monkees in the mid-Sixties), many artists – particularly rock singers – could argue that session musicians had no soul and no interest in the music they performed.

Until the Sound of the Mersey hit an unsuspecting world, the sixties produced no radical changes. The wholesome-sweet voice of Roy Orbison took the honours in the charts whenever Elvis left No.1 untenanted. There was plenty of room for Max Bygraves, Anthony Newley, Helen Shapiro, Connie Stevens, Bobby Vee, Duane Eddy and the vigorous fifteen-year-old Brenda Lee. The Beach Boys brought the sound of sunlight and surf to the less salubrious cities, Johnny Kidd and the Pirates kept the heavy end of rock going with *Shakin' All Over* and the Everly Brothers nudged the King and Big O away from No.1 with *Lucille* and *Cathy's Clown*.

The Tin Pan Alleys of both the USA and Britain were following the old formulas with a little adaptation to the times, Radio Luxembourg's Top Twenty was still based on sheet music sales and Family Favourites vied with Jack Jackson as the main plugger of the latest disc. Though Kennedy and Carr had split up, the latter was writing *Kon Tiki* and *Man Of Mystery* for the Shadows – one of the first instrumental groups – and Kennedy was giving a hit to the unlikely Ken Dodd (*Love Is Like A Violin*) and the very likely Petula Clark (*Romeo*). Rodgers and Hammerstein were back with *The Flower Drum Song* and Lionel Bart's *Oliver* conquered the West End.

There was nothing really disturbing in the wind. Rhythm and blues, on the whole, was ignored in Britain and was mildly popular in the States. The Isley Brothers, Bo Diddley and James Brown had some interested followers in the UK but it was Jimmy Jones, Johnny Preston, Bobby Vee and Conway Twitty who had the big audiences. Acker Bilk's *Summer Set* followed the fad for trad and there were few critics of the craze. Kenny Ball got himself a gold disc for *Midnight In Moscow* in '61 and Lonnie Donegan pipped this with three gold discs for *Rock Island Line*, *My Old Man's A Dustman* and *Does Your Chewing Gum Lose Its Flavour*. Matt Monro turned out the smooth ballads like *Portrait Of My Love* and never quite took off, and there were death songs like Ricky Valances' *Tell Laura I Love Her* which the BBC banned.

There was a liking for the boy/girl harmonies of Nina and Frederick and Micki and Griff, though the Beverley Sisters, despite joining Liberace at the London Palladium, distinctly belonged to the Fifties. Their male equivalents, the King Brothers, had also peaked their popularity in the Fifties with *A White Sports Coat* and *Mais Oui*.

Jerry Lordan, composer of 'Apache', with Bert Corri and Kay O'Dwyer of Francis, Day & Hunter

Cliff Richard was Britain's number one heart-throb with a gold disc for *Living Doll* and the Shadows, not to be outdone, got a gold and an Ivor Novello award for Jerry Lordan's *Apache*. So did Anthony Newley for *What Kind Of Fool Am I* but he wouldn't play the pop game and headed for the musicals of Broadway.

Chubby Checker gave a few hearts a missed beat with *The Twist* – which also strained a few backs. It's still around and had a brief revival in the Seventies, but its success, like that of the cha cha, was due more to a desire for something new than its inate appeal. Strangely enough, dancing has not developed for the last fifteen years, remaining as much an isolated exhibition as something shared with a partner.

Acker Bilk got a No.1 in the UK and the USA with *Stranger On The Shore* and sold 40,000 copies of the sheet music to get an Ivor Novello Award. Frank Ifield got three number ones in a row and Frankie Vaughan could still wow the girls by throwing out a leg, while from the States the folk music of Peter, Paul and Mary, Pete Seeger, the Kingston Trio and Joan Baez came across with a message that would later be labelled 'protest'. There was a poet blowing a harmonica and singing disturbing songs, but poets were not wanted just yet in Britain and Dylan remained virtually unsung in the UK.

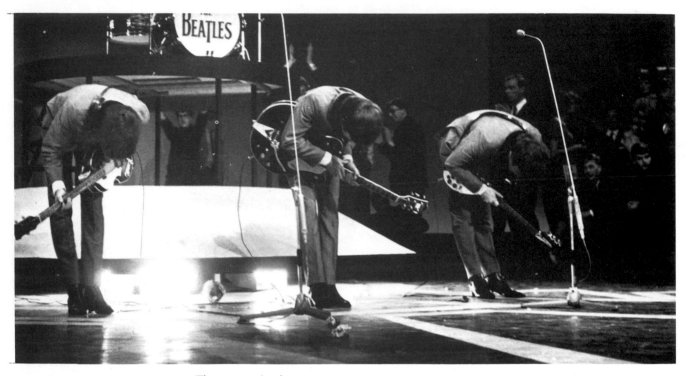

Those were the days, my friend

Then came the Beatles. They were nowhere men from nowhere land. Liverpool, despite its abundance of comedians and reputation for Scouse wit, was an unlikely place for the birth of a world phenomenon. It was a big Anglo-Irish port, boozy, puritanical, Catholic, tough and uncompromising in its rejection of non-Liverpudlians. It was also badly hit by Hitler and subsequently by the town council who, between them, have now destroyed the city's individuality.

The Beatles were just about Liverpudlians, coming from the suburbs of the city, and Brian Epstein put it all together for them. And with them, a million others.

Skiffle had left a conviction among its followers that you could not only listen to music, you could make it yourself. In sheds, garages, bedrooms and clubs all over England, musical rows of varying degrees of competence were shaking the earth. Before the advent of the ubiquitous discos and their jockeys, a group with reasonable ability could get a date – a gig – without much trouble, even if the amplifiers were small and possibly lethal and the choice of chords restricted to three. Some of the noise was chronic but it enabled many to become active participants rather than passive listeners.

The Beatles made it for themselves, and for a generation. They brought with them the

Gerry and the Pacemakers

Mersey sound of Gerry and the Pacemakers, the Merseybeats, the Searchers, the Swinging Blue Jeans. The group became all, each member a part of the whole. Soon anyone could make it and often did. In Liverpool, we felt that we were the chosen; we all knew someone who knew someone in the charts, had an anecdote to tell about some bright new star. The Top Twenty was dominated by groups, the Dave Clark Five, Billy J. Kramer and the Dakotas, the Animals, Manfred Mann, the Mojos, they came and went with the surge of the tide.

America fell. There had been, in those early Beatle recordings, the usual hint of an American twang, the emulation which most British singers felt obliged to make. But as the States were successfully invaded by the Beatles, the Dave Clark Five, Herman's Hermits and, to a lesser extent at first, the Rolling Stones, the need to fall in with the American image declined and it was America which became a colony for British music.

The States replied as they should. The Beach Boys grew their hair and the Byrds were acclaimed as America's answer to the Beatles; so were the Monkees before their cardboard image collapsed. With the Beatles – and the Stones – seal of approval, the

The Searchers

167

Otis Redding

rhythm and blues of Otis Redding, James Brown, Chuck Berry, Mary Wells, Martha and the Vandellas brought both rock and soul back into the charts, to be combined by the frenetic Jimi Hendrix. Tamla Motown began its boom with Little Stevie Wonder, Diana Ross and the Supremes, the Temptations, and Ike and Tina Turner.

It is now a habit to refer to the Beatles as a rock group – even a band – but they were not regarded as such in their first few years of popularity. Rock was a little old-fashioned, old hat, out-dated. Besides, in the mid-Sixties, pop songs were still not so closely defined into specific areas although rhythm and blues predominated by 1965.

Any type of song could be a hit. Roy Orbison could sob *It's Over* or rock with *Pretty Woman*, the Animals could smoulder about a New Orleans Brothel *The House Of The Rising Sun*, the Kinks scowled through *You Really Got Me* and the Stones chanted *It's All Over Now* with Mick Jagger frightening hell out of momma and poppa. Cilla Black, with more than a hint of Scouse, gave more than a hint of voice with *Anyone Who Had A Heart*, while Lulu gave a definite suggestion of over-stretched vocal chords with *Shout*. Pop folk saw the Seekers with a constant flow of hits and Donovan and Dylan began to put blood into the body of protest songs. Tom Jones and Englebert Humperdink fulfilled the traditions of showbusiness personality, offering glamour, sex and sweat to eager hands on both sides of the Atlantic. Some good songs too.

So the Beatles wrote and played music that could not be restricted to a single category. The standard *Yesterday* was as different to the near-rock *Twist And Shout* as *Girl* was to *Can't Buy Me Love*.

But one category that they did belong to, more than any other, was youth. By 1967 the values and traditions nurtured by previous generations had been all but wiped out by the massive disregard of youth. Some of it was good, the sense of belonging to a world in which you could make it; some of it was more or less daft, like the excesses of Flower Power. Catered for and applauded from all sides, with the money to indulge in any desires, the children of the Swinging Sixties mouthed slogans, snatched handfuls of drugs, opened boutiques by the score, preened themselves in psychedelic lighting and stored up questionable wisdom handed out by gurus of both Eastern and Western worlds. The bad taste of the Sixties, the acceptance of anything as an 'art form' and the instant acclaim accorded by the media to any second-rate junketing pursued us into the Seventies. Only harder times have made us look twice.

In an Age of Superlatives, when anything could be the latest craze, it was inevitable that the Beatles should be pushed beyond the barriers which they may not have wanted to cross, that constant attention should have given more importance to them than they warranted. They were good at what they did musically and that says enough. It was as well that they finally broke up in 1970; they might have found it difficult to find a niche today and it was fitting that a legend should have a final end rather than a slow fade out.

Some of the above applies to the Rolling Stones. A good rhythm and blues rock group overtaken by its image, their performances were spectacular shows of music, glitter, light and noise. A future generation, listening to a Stone's LP, might wonder what all the fuss was about.

Cilla Black

The period from 1968 to the present saw a split in popular music, a split between the comfortable – the cosiness of the Osmonds and the clean-cut features of John Denver – and the uncomfortable personified by the foulness of Alice Cooper and the nastiness of punk rock. Tin Pan Alley lost out altogether, once the Beatles set the fashion for singer-written songs. Many artists started their own record companies – Emerson, Lake & Palmer set up Monticore, Elton John started Rocket Records – and a publishing company could be set up just to handle the proceeds of one song.

Fashions in music smouldered, flared and went out as fame was more short-lived and stars proved to be unenduring, often simply because of the strain implicit in just keeping going. Reggae brought its West Indian beat into London's pop scene and is still – just about – with us. Glitter-rock and glam-rock hit the teeny-boppers as Gary Glitter camped it up on stage and kids screamed as they were supposed to do. The supergroups of Emerson, Lake & Palmer, Led Zeppelin and Genesis crashed into heavy-metal rock to blow out the kids' minds and punk rock was created out of the inheritance from the Stones and Slade.

'Manias' were plenty. The ageing fans of the Sixties gathered at Wembley to give a last homage to the Stones who stopped rolling. David Bowie received adulation from

Queen

undefined quarters in the manner of an aloof bisexual god. David Essex and David Cassidy smiled toothily at their pre-adolescent fans and suddenly there was a craze for ragtime with Joshua Rifkin giving slightly lifeless renderings of the works of Scott Joplin.

The over-indulged violence of Jimi Hendrix, the smashing of guitars and amplifiers by the Who, and the exhibitionist uncaring violence put forward by the Stones, typified in *Street Fighting Man*, led to the squalid fascination for Alice Cooper on the one hand, and a mournful nostalgia for the past on the other. Glenn Miller swung back into the Top Twenty with *In The Mood* in 1975, many hits of the Sixties were revived with age-ing ravers like Neil Sedaka back in the charts and there were even direct imitations of hits from a more secure world, as with Hoagy Carmichael's *My Resistance Is Low*.

The charts continued to yield up the same type of 'pop tunes' which would have been hits in the Fifties and Sixties – *I'd Like to Teach The World To Sing* of the New Seekers, *Maggie May* of Rod Stewart, *Long Haired Lover From Liverpool* of Little Jimmy Osmond – and even the musical theatre was able to offer up hits from the quasi-religious *Jesus Christ Superstar* and *Godspell*.

But as Bob Dylan so rightly put it, the times they are a-changin' and they had changed for Francis, Day & Hunter. Though Radio Luxembourg's Top Twenty was based on music sales until the Sixties (sheet music was often bought purely for the lyrics), it was records which people were buying to listen to, not sheets to plunk out notes with one finger on the disappearing piano. As popular music became increasingly dependent on electronics, and therefore increasingly difficult to reproduce at home – or even on the stage for some groups – so the music sheets had less relevance to the hit number. Heavy metal rock does not lend itself to sheet music.

10 C.C.

Rod Stewart, superiax exile

So sheet sales continued to decline and Francis, Day & Hunter relied more and more on buying hits from the States and taking over competitors like Bert Feldman, acquired in 1953.

This gave the publishers an excellent catalogue but provided no solution for Britain's Tin Pan Alley. In the early Sixties Bert Corri, the guiding hand of F, D & H, said in Eddie Rogers' *Tin Pan Alley* 'Sales of sheet music today are practically nil. It's all records today. Today's music? I don't think much of it – there are too many at it, churning out far too many songs. In the old days songs were made by the artists over the footlights.' But for Bert and all the Alley, the old days were over. The Beatles, to be sure, made their own songs over the footlights, but they published the songs themselves, and the group boom left few pickings for Tin Pan Alley. Composers sang their own material and, although there were exceptions like the F, D & H songs of Herman's Hermits and the Dave Clark Five, the new groups found new publishers for their songs.

The Alley was no longer at the centre of things by the end of the Fifties. Winifred Atwell's piano had sold thousands of sheets for F, D & H but pianos gave way to the guitar except for occasional hits. Though Julie Andrews and Frankie Vaughan may have been frequent visitors to Charing Cross Road, the real action belonged to the record companies and it was inevitable that the biggest, EMI, should eventually acquire the best, F, D & H (and its subsidiaries), as the Swinging Sixties gave way to the Seventies.

Then, too, F, D & H had lost the impetus of a family business determined to succeed. It had succeeded, it had seen the best days of the Alley and it continued to tread water ably as the turbulence of the late Sixties took away all certainties in popular music. But Fred Day died at ninety-seven, still believing that he could write hit songs under pseudonyms such as Alter Ego and Edward Montagu and still not quite producing that hit. With him went much of the personal drive of the Day family. Eddie Day, who had taken over from Fred, soldiered on manfully but David Day, who had the final say, saw family music publishing as a declining business and opted out.

The days of the song pluggers were over, the feeling for a hit, the melody line on the piano in the pub, the excitement of the band striking up to play your song. The record companies inherited the music and wagged the tail of the dog which had started them and it is inevitable that music publishing, in the world of popular music and its attendant outlets today, should be a part of record production.

The F, D & H catalogue is a history of popular music, a bag of riches to reach into when needed, as happened recently when the *Trail Of The Lonesome Pine* was resurrected. Though new songs will not appear under the F, D & H imprint, there are plenty of old ones which will remain a while yet.

How much longer any popular song will remain around is anyone's guess. My guess carries no more weight than yours – I have no crystal earphones to plug me into the hits of the future. But for what it is worth, my guess is my last chapter.

TOO YOUNG

Words by SYLVIA DEE   Music by SID LIPPMAN

Recorded by
NAT "KING" COLE
on CAPITOL CL13564.

1/-

THE SUN MUSIC PUBLISHING Co. LTD., 23, Denmark St., London, W.C.2.

TOO YOUNG

Words by
SYLVIA DEE

Music by
SID LIPPMAN

They try to tell us we're too young _____ Too young to

real-ly be in love. _____ They say that love's a word, a

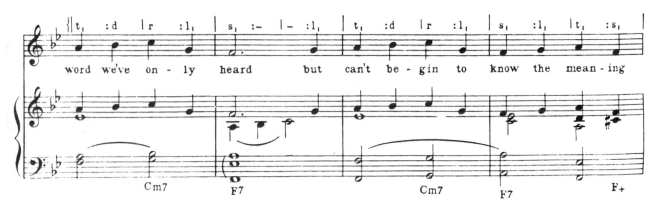

word we've on-ly heard but can't be-gin to know the mean-ing

S. M. Co. Ltd. 1715

Kisses Sweeter Than Wine

Words by
PAUL CAMPBELL

Music by
JOEL NEWMAN

F. & D. Ltd.22585

CRY

Words & Music by
CHURCHILL KOHLMAN

1/-

FRANCIS, DAY & HUNTER LTD.
138/140, CHARING CROSS ROAD,
LONDON - W.C.2.

CRY

F.& D.Ltd. 22413

AIN'T THAT A SHAME

Words & Music by ANTOINE DOMINO & DAVE BARTHOLOMEW

Recorded by
PAT BOONE
on LONDON HLD 8172.

FRANCIS, DAY & HUNTER LTD, 138-140, CHARING CROSS RD, LONDON, W.C.2

Ain't That A Shame!

Words and Music by
ANTOINE DOMINO and
DAVE BARTHOLOMEW

1 You made me cry when you said____ Good-
2 (You) broke my heart when you said____ we'll

-bye part Ain't that a shame!____ My tears fell like rain____

Ain't that a shame!____ You're the one to blame.____

F. & D. Ltd. 23133.

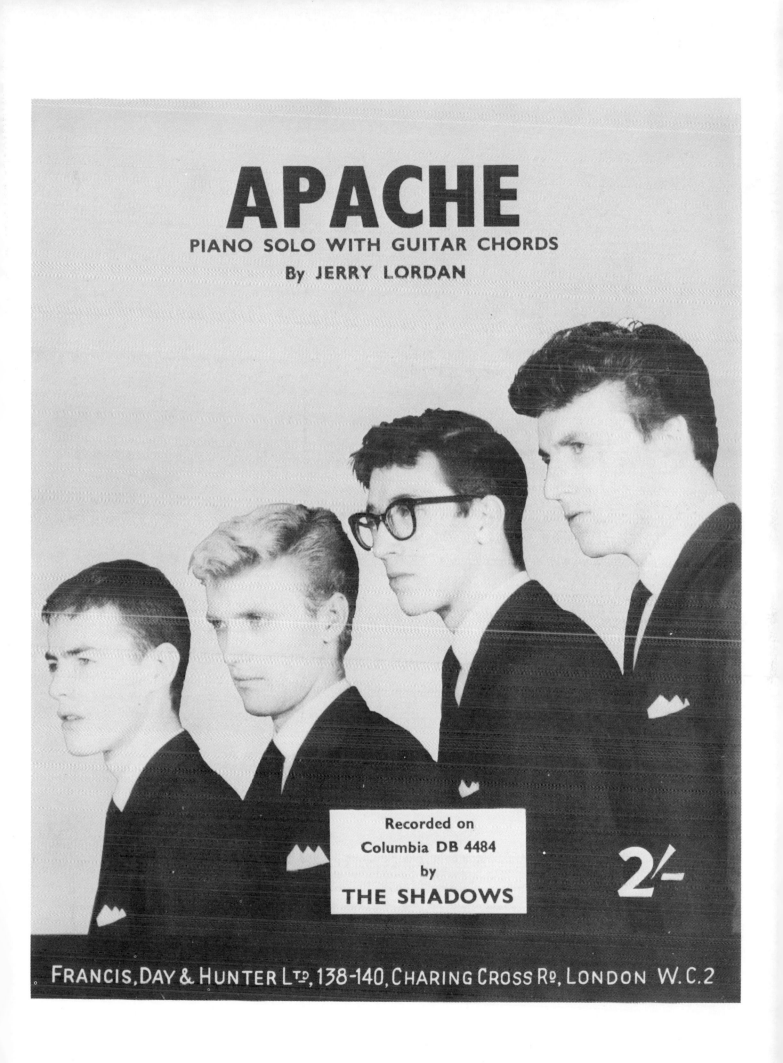

ÆPACHE

By JERRY LORDAN

F. & D. Ltd. 23721b

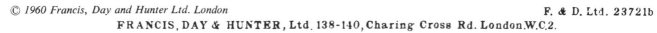

FRANCIS, DAY & HUNTER, Ltd. 138-140, Charing Cross Rd. London.W.C.2.

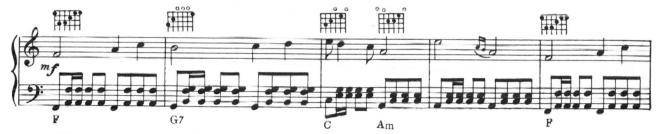

F. & D. Ltd. 23721b

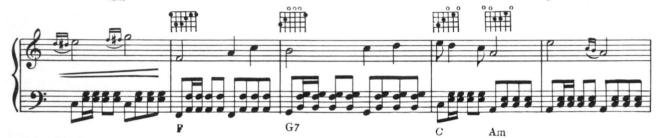

F. & D. Ltd. 23721b

THE LAST WALTZ

BY LES REED & BARRY MASON

Donna Music Limited Sole Selling Agents:-
FRANCIS, DAY & HUNTER LTD., 138/140, Charing Cross Road, London, W.C.2.

3/-

THE LAST WALTZ

LES REED &
BARRY MASON

D. M. Ltd. 1021

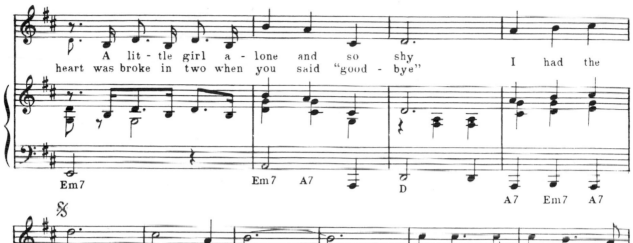

A lit - tle girl a - lone and so shy
heart was broke in two when you said "good - bye"
I had the

Em7   Em7 A7   D   A7 Em7 A7

last waltz with you _____ Two lone - ly peo - ple to -

D   Dmaj7   Gmaj7   G6   A7   Em A7

- geth - er _____ I fell in love with you The

D   D7+   G

to Coda ⊕ 1

last waltz should last for ev - er.

Em7 (A Bass)   A7   D

D.M. Ltd. 1021

ev - er. It's all o - ver now no-thing left to say Just my

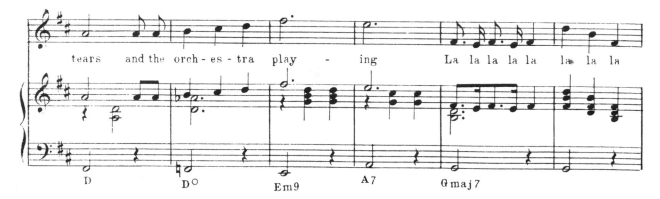

tears and the orch-es-tra play - ing La la la la la la la la

la _____ La la la la la la la la la I had the

CODA

ev - er La la la la la la la la la

Printed in England by WEST CENTRAL PRINTING CO. LTD. London.

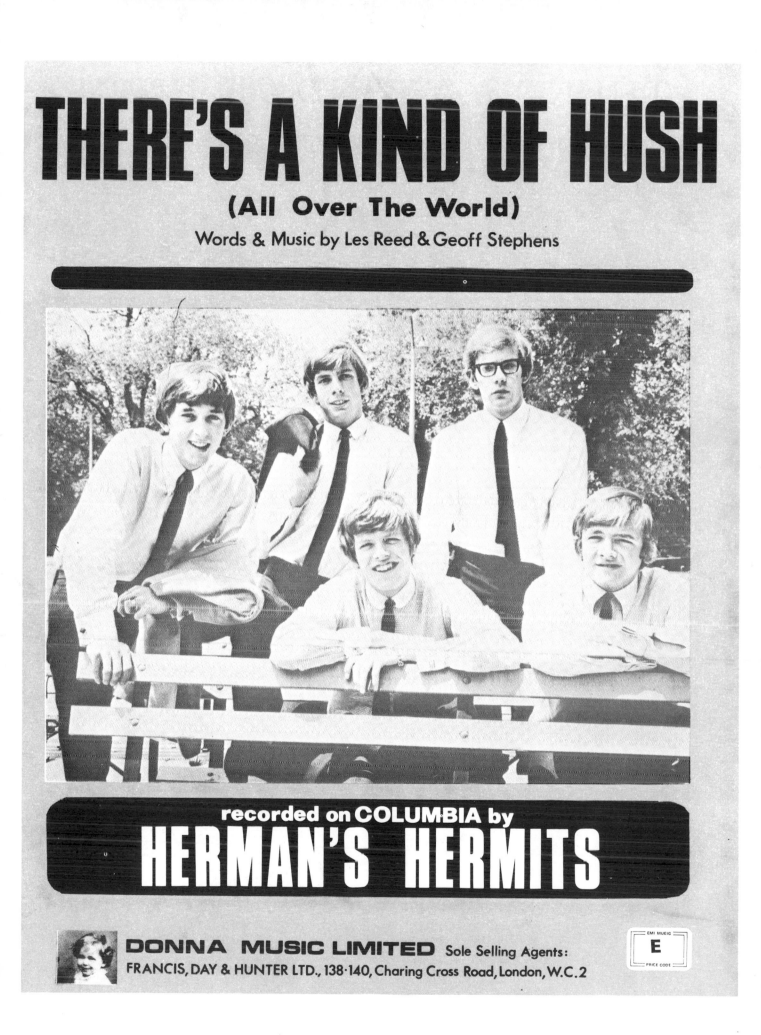

THERE'S A KIND OF HUSH
(ALL OVER THE WORLD)

Words and Music by

LES REED &
GEOFF STEPHENS

Medium tempo (With a beat)

There's a kind of hush all over the world Tonight all over the world You can hear the sounds of lovers in love You know what I mean. Just the

D.M.Ltd.1014

two of us   and no-bo-dy else—   in sight   There's no-bo-dy else—

Bb   D7   Gm   Bb7

— and I'm feel-ing   good—   just hold-ing you tight —   So

Eb   F7   Bb   Db7

lis-ten ve-ry care - ful-ly—   Clos-er   now   and you—   will see what I mean

Eb   Eb6   Ebmaj7   Eb6

It is-n't a dream.   The

Bb   Bb7

Printed in England by WEST CENTRAL PRINTING CO. LTD., London WIP IAD.

196

DELILAH

Words & Music by
LES REED & BARRY MASON

D. M. Ltd. 1038

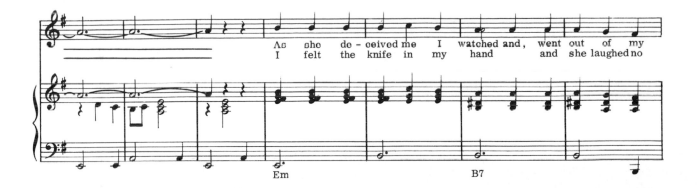

As she de-ceived me I watched and, went out of my
I felt the knife in my hand and she laughed no

Em   B7

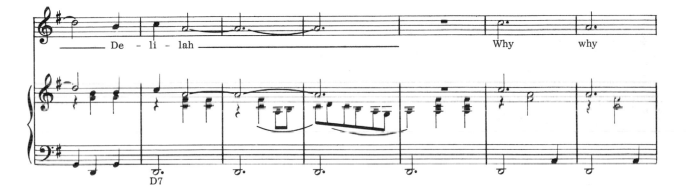

mind _____
more _____   } My   my   my _____

Em   D7   G 7

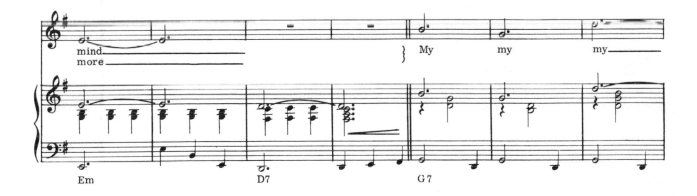

De - li - lah _____   Why   why

D7

why _____   De - li - lah _____   I _____
So _____

F# G   G

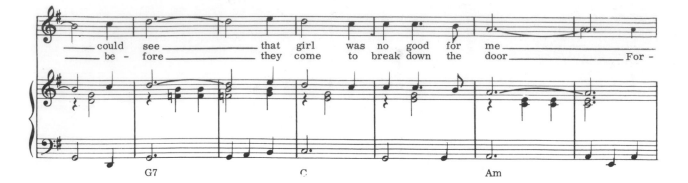

could see _____ that girl was no good for me
be - fore _____ they come to break down the door _____ For -

G7   C   Am

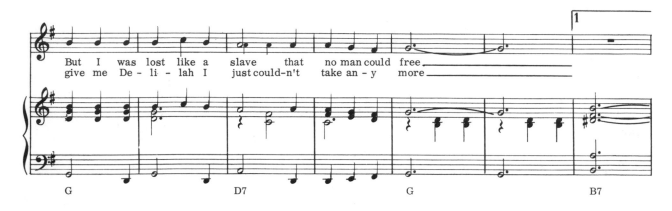

But I was lost like a slave that no man could free _____
give me De - li - lah I just could-n't take an - y more _____

G   D7   G   B7

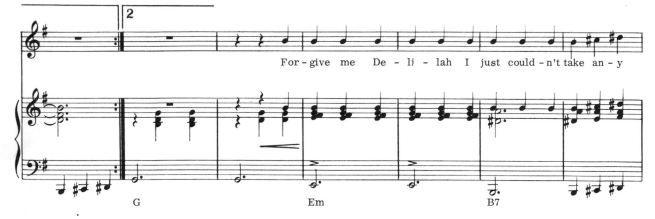

For - give me De - li - lah I just could -n't take an - y

G   Em   B7

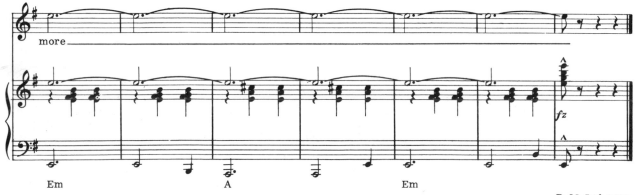

more _____

Em   A   Em

D. M. Ltd. 1038

Printed in England by WEST CENTRAL PRINTING CO. LTD. London.

Le Moribond
(SEASONS IN THE SUN)

French lyric by
JACQUES BREL

1st Refrain

Adieu l'Émile, je t'aimais bien,
Adieu l'Émile, je t'aimais bien, tu sais,
On a chanté les mêmes vins,
On a chanté les mêmes filles,
On a chanté les mêm's chagrins,
Adieu l'Émile, je vais mourir.
C'est dur de mourir au printemps, tu sais,
Mais j'pars aux fleurs la paix dans l'âme
Car vu qu't'es bon comme du pain blanc,
Je sais qu'tu prendras soin d'ma femme.

2nd Refrain

Adieu Curé, je t'aimais bien,
Adieu Curé, je t'aimais bien, tu sais,
On n'était pas du même bord,
On n'était pas du mêm' chemin,
Mais on cherchait le même port.
Adieu Curé, je vais mourir.
C'est dur de mourir au printemps, tu sais,
Mais j'pars aux fleurs la paix dans l'âme
Car vu qu't'étais son confident,
Je sais qu'tu prendras soin d'ma femme.

3rd Refrain

Adieu l'Antoine, j't'aimais pas bien,
Adieu l'Antoine, j't'aimais pas bien, tu sais,
J'en crève de crever aujourd'hui
Alors que toi t'es bien vivant
Et mêm' plus solid' que l'ennui.
Adieu l'Antoine, je vais mourir.
C'est dur de mourir au printemps, tu sais,
Mais j'pars aux fleurs la paix dans l'âme
Car vu que t'étais son amant,
Je sais qu'tu prendras soin d'ma femme.

4th Refrain

Adieu ma femme, je t'aimais bien,
Adieu ma femme, je t'aimais bien, tu sais,
Mais je prend l'train pour le Bon Dieu,
Je prend le train qu'est avant l'tien,
Mais on prend tous le train qu'on peut.
Adieu ma femme, je vais mourir.
C'est dur de mourir au printemps, tu sais,
Mais j'pars aux fleurs les yeux fermés ma femme
Car vu qu'j'les ai fermés souvent,
Je sais qu'tu prendras soin d'mon âme.

Chorus

J'veux qu'on rie, J'veux qu'on danse,
J'veux qu'on s'amus' comm' des fous,
J'veux qu'on rie, J'veux qu'on danse,
Quand c'est qu'on m'mettra dans l'trou.

Francis, Day & Hunter Ltd., 138/140, Charing Cross Road, London, W.C.2.

Seasons 1

Seasons in the Sun
(Le Moribond)

English lyric by
ROD McKUEN

Music by
JACQUES BREL

Folk ballad style (moderato)

Piano

Chorus

We had joy, we had fun, we had sea-sons in the sun; But the
lives we had fun, we had sea-sons in the sun; But the

hills we would climb were just sea-sons out of time.
stars we could reach were just star-fish on the beach.

(to Fine last time)

1. All our
2. *(Segue to Verse)*

Fine

beach.

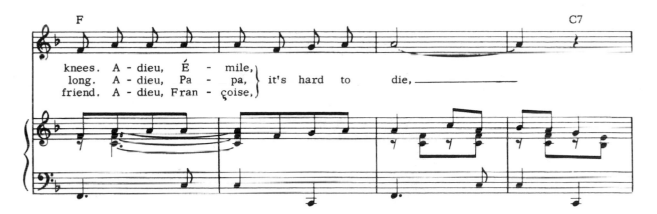

knees. A - dieu, É - mile,⎫
long. A - dieu, Pa - pa,⎬ it's hard to die, _____
friend. A - dieu, Fran - çoise,⎭

When all the birds are sing-ing in the sky; Now that the

spring is in the air, _____ Pret - ty girls are ev - 'ry -
Lit - tle chil - dren ev - 'ry -
With your lov - ers ev - 'ry -

3rd time al Fine

where; _____ Think of me and I'll be there. We had
where; _____ When you'll see them, I'll be there. We had
where; _____ Just be care - ful, I'll be there. All our

3rd time al Fine

Seasons 4

6
STARGAZING

When the Rolling Stones made their first television appearance, the audience watched with shocked curiosity, almost mesmerised with amazement. America didn't at first accept them, ignoring them for the more traditional image of the Dave Clark Five.

But the Stones prevailed and turned the exception into the rule. They, their followers and their imitators set the fashion. Gradually we came to accept their standards and their life style, and some accepted their philosophy which they could afford to nourish.

This raises the interesting question of who exactly sets the fashion? Were the Stones really expressing some deep-felt grievance of the young, some need to reject 'the values of society' and start a revolution? Or was the image and the taste manufactured, was the mood deep-seated or was it planted, fertilised and harvested by those whose interest lay in its ultimate yield?

In the age of multi-media, where one leads, the other is sure to follow. If films use sex and violence as a bait to draw the ingenuous and the impressionable, then it follows that music may well do the same, particularly if the manufacturing companies have fingers in both pies. Thus punk rock is born. The old clichés are trotted out – 'new' and 'exciting', 'in the forefront of the movement', 'responding to a need'. And those responsible for the promotion scuttle back to their comfortable suburbia, leaving the fires they lit to burn themselves out on others.

Yet the nihilistic crudeness of punk rock is just as much a reflection of our times as the Charleston was of the Twenties and the crooners of the Thirties. To some extent, fashions in popular music were always manufactured. But from the Beatles onwards, popular music no longer conformed to the perceived standards of society; it reigned in its own kingdom and scorned those who did not accept or observe its own rituals. Eventually, with its promoters and its pushers, its access to television, radio and the press, and its ability to restrict its listeners to a constant diet of its own philosophy, it was inevitable that a form of music would emerge which would be diametrically opposed to the objectives of the society in which it had been nourished.

All this, of course, is too black, too pessimistic and popular music will no doubt ride out its own storms. Though the days when a composer's name, like Cole Porter, could comfortably span several decades and draw an automatic enthusiastic response from an audience, are well and truly over, a good song or an exciting sound still has its basic appeal and the Top Twenty of 1977 is no cause for despair. Although there are only limited sales for the sheet music of current pops, the music shops are very busy. There is a consistent demand for standard songs and for the attractive compilation albums that now represent a major part of the music sellers' business. The retail F, D & H shop in Charing Cross Road, which has been selling music for an hundred years, was completely redesigned in 1974 and is now experiencing the highest sales ever for printed music.

So what can one predict about the future of popular music?

Well, its going to become more and more fragmented, as specialised interests turn away from the general run of pop music as determined by Radio One and the commercial stations. Radio One will be forced, increasingly, to cater for a teeny-bopper audience and the banalities of the D.J.s will fall on the deaf ears of those for whom radio is no answer at all.

Singers will not get any younger unless we inexplicably seek out another Shirley Temple in our longing to find a good ship lollipop. Indeed, singers may well get older if the supergroups, already ageing in pop terms, keep some of their popularity.

Nostalgia, too, will play its part, each generation plundering its past for its own sound. Indeed, those of us who were part of the swinging Sixties use the 'teeny-bopper' term with some malice, hardly able to believe that our day of determining the current pop scene has passed and that the play goes on without us. No doubt Bill Haley, like any good book which goes into its umpteenth reprint, will continue to add to his twenty-six million sales of *Rock Around The Clock* long after the clock has struck midnight for him. If Laurel and Hardy can rise from the grave, why should it stop there? More than likely, where copyright permits, there will be a Nostalgia Top Twenty to go with soul, reggae, rock and singles.

Popular music will lose its importance, will cease to be a life style. Already it is burning itself out. There will be hits, of course, and some of these will sell in millions, but the decline in pop's importance will remain unchecked until it becomes merely one of several diversions – which is possibly where it should belong.

The music publishers, like F, D & H, are inextricably and inevitably tied to the record industry which will have to diversify more and more to cater for widely differing tastes. With fierce competition carving up a reduced market, the popularity of cassette recorders and the difficulty of preventing illegal recording, and the shrinkage of export markets abroad as indigenous companies claim their own stake, there could be rough times ahead.

So long as there are musicals with the quality of *Cabaret* and *A Chorus Line*, the theatre is not likely to decline, particularly with the huge fund of revivals available. It is curious, though, that a show such as *A Chorus Line* should produce no individual hit to remember it by. Such hits are needed to ensure that the popularity of the musical is not confined to the capital cities.

Perhaps music will make its re-appearance in the home as something you perform as well as something that you listen to. True, heavy metal rock is difficult to perform in the front room without tolerant and deaf neighbours, but live music in pubs is ever-popular and encompasses jazz, blues, rock and folk, all of which can be practised in the garage. When sheet music sales overtake record sales, a real revolution will be taking place.

Then, too, in the next decade, another phenomenon may be found to ride the waves of success which bore the Beatles. God knows, the promoters are trying hard enough, veering from the sugary sweetness of the Osmonds, the good-living of the Bay City Rollers, the don't touch-me-I'm-beyond-it-all of David Bowie and the snarl of the Sex

Bay City Rollers

Pistols. But the phenomenon, if and when it happens, is as unpredictable now as the Beatles were in 1960.

Predictions, anyway, are little more than a projection of one's own bias and no doubt time will show me to be wrong on all counts.

So, we've more or less covered one hundred years in these chapters and I hope the trip has been worthwhile. Some stations have been missed out on the way but the pace has been fast rather than leisurely and the omissions, I trust, do not detract from the whole.

And though you surely won't plough through these chapters again, it's a nice thought – for me – that you will keep returning to this book to hear that song again. Play it again, Sam.

Sam playing it in CASABLANCA
(*Dooley Wilson, Humphrey Bogart and Ingrid Bergman*)